Cadbury's
SIXTH BOOK OF
CHILDREN'S POETRY

Beaver Books

A Beaver Book
Published by Arrow Books Limited
62-5 Chandos Place, London WC2N 4NW
An imprint of Century Hutchinson Ltd

London Melbourne Sydney Auckland
Johannesburg and agencies throughout the world

First published 1988
© Cadbury Ltd 1988

Set in Souvenir Light by
JH Graphics Limited, Reading

Made and printed in Great Britain
by Cox & Wyman Ltd
Reading, Berks

ISBN 0 09 955430 5

Contents

Publisher's note

The poems in this book were chosen by a panel of judges which included poets, teachers and education-alists, from nearly 40,000 entries for the Cadbury's National Exhibition of Children's Poetry, Art and Crafts Exhibition 1988/89. This year is the sixth in which there has been a poetry section and the judges — Jennifer Curry, anthologist and author; Peter Porter, poet and literary journalist; Gareth Owen, poet, novelist and playwright; and Michael Rosen, children's author, poet and anthologist — were delighted at the great variety of material. They chose as outstanding the work of Siobhan Aiton and Claire Milne, whose poems appear on pages 98 and 108, and 198 and 220 respectively. Siobhan and Claire are the Italian Tour Award winners for 1988.

Siobhan Aiton comes from Llangefni on Angelsey and is fifteen years old. She plans to take 'A' level English and Welsh and then possibly go on to do a writing course. As well as poetry, she also enjoys writing for her local youth theatre. Her numerous hobbies include rock-climbing and working with horses.

Fifteen-year-old Claire Milne lives in Urmston, Manchester. She is currently studying for 'A' levels in English, French and History and hopes to read English at university. As well as poetry, she also writes short stories and is particularly interested in science fiction and fantasy. She also likes the theatre, swim-ming and playing the piano.

The Arthur Lines Poetry Award was given to Lara Mair whose poems appear on pages 80, 105 and 130. The judges also highly commended 31 children whose

4

poems appear on pages 12, 14, 18, 20, 28, 30, 33, 36, 38, 42, 58, 70, 86, 110, 114, 116, 141, 144, 148, 154, 166, 175, 182, 184, 187, 189, 194, 212, 222 and 227.

The poems have been arranged under subjects, which gives the reader the opportunity to compare the ideas of children from as young as six to mature seventeen year olds. All the illustrations are taken from entries to the Art and Craft section of this year's Exhibition, and they complement the poems in an unusual and pleasing way.

We are very happy to be publishing such an interesting and original book and would like to thank all the writers and artists for their superb efforts. Don't forget, there's another chance to see your poem in print in the Seventh Cadbury's Book of Poetry to be published in 1989. For details on how to enter next year's exhibition please turn to page 232.

Cadbury Limited and the Publishers have taken every possible precaution to ensure that the material in this book is the original work of the named writers and does not infringe the copyright of any person or body. Each poem has been authenticated by a responsible adult and the work has been carefully checked by independent experts for plagiarism. If, despite this, we have inadvertently failed to identify any borrowed poem we would be grateful if this could be brought to our attention for correction at the first opportunity.

Foreword

The poetry section of the National Exhibition of Children's Art has once again attracted a high number of entries from young poets all over the country. The judges had a difficult task in making their selection but were unanimous in their choice for the Italian Art Tour winners whose work they felt showed tremendous promise.

The Arthur Lines Poetry Award goes this year to an outstanding young poet whose bright, fresh and thought-provoking verses were much admired by the judges.

We were pleased to welcome three distinguished new judges and are very grateful to all our poetry panel for giving their time and expertise. Whilst our judges understand the need for 'theme' work, they would like to encourage more creative freedom for children to write from their own experiences.

We would like to thank the judges for their continuing support for Cadbury's National Exhibition of Children's Art, as well as the teachers, parents and children without whose continued enthusiasm there would be no Poetry Book or Exhibition.

Poetry has been given more emphasis within the Exhibition itself and we are especially pleased that young poets at every venue we have visited on our national tour have had the opportunity to broadcast their work.

Cadbury will again this year donate royalties from the sale of this book to the Save The Children Fund.

Adrian Cadbury.

N.B. *Details of dates and venues where Cadbury's National Exhibition of Children's Art will be on display are given on page 10*

Cadbury's Sixth Book of Children's Poetry

AWARD WINNERS – Poetry Section
41st National Exhibition of Children's Art 1988/89

1988 ITALIAN TOUR AWARD
Siobhan Aiton (15)
Ysgol Gyfun, Llangefni, Anglesey, Gwynedd
Claire Milne (15)
Urmston, Manchester

SCHOOL POETRY AWARDS
7 and under
St John's R.C. First School, Norwich, Norfolk
8–11
Northmead County Middle School, Guildford, Surrey
12–14
Halesworth Middle School, Halesworth, Suffolk
15–17
Debenham High School, Stowmarket, Suffolk

ARTHUR LINES POETRY AWARD
Lara Mair (12) Halesworth Middle School, Halesworth, Suffolk

HIGHLY COMMENDED
7 and under
Edward Cooper (7) St Johns R.C. First School, Norwich, Norfolk
Erika Cottle (7) Long Credon C. Combined School, Long Credon,
Aylesbury, Bucks
Kate Dempsey (7) Keele, Staffs
Natasha Gammon (6) Cheslyn Hay, Walsall, W. Midlands
Adele Inugai-Dixon (4) Stoke Park, Ipswich
Edward Mooney (7) St Johns R.C. First School, Norwich, Norfolk
Vincent Muddle (6) Whitehills Lower School, Kingsthorpe, Northampton

8–11
Samantha Budworth (11) St Mary's Gate School, Southbourne, Dorset
Rachael Girven (11) Manor Junior School, Birkenhead, Merseyside
Franklin Puddefoot (10) Weston Turville C.E. Combined School, Weston
Turville, Bucks

Nathanael Selman (11) Exeter, Devon
Catherine Smart (11) London
Kelly Smith (11) Halesworth Middle School, Halesworth, Suffolk

12–14

Sarah Baxter (14) The Mountbatten School, Romsey, Hants
Danny Connors (14) Debenham High School, Stowmarket, Suffolk
James Crawford (13) The King's School, Canterbury, Kent
Chloe Downs (14) St Edward School, Charlton Kings, Cheltenham, Glos
Rachel Harvey (14) Monmouth Comprehensive School, Monmouth, Gwent
Emma McCulloch (13) Ewell High School, West Ewell, Surrey
Neal Patel (14) Cardiff High School, Cardiff
Heather Tewkesbury (13) Stourport-on-Severn High School, Stourport-on-Severn, Worcs
Nichola White (12) Minehead Middle School, Minehead, Somerset
Catherine Wilkinson (13) Buckden, Huntingdon, Cambs

15–17

Kathryn Boydell (15) Stockport, Cheshire
Catherine Burkinshaw (16) Haydon Hill, Aylesbury, Bucks
Clare Connors (15) Debenham High School, Stowmarket, Suffolk
Robert McGregor (15) Debenham High School, Stowmarket, Suffolk
Imane Massoud (15) The International School of London, London
Karen Taylor (15) Tarporley, Cheshire
Simon Wales (15) Lichfield, Stockport, Cheshire

41st Exhibition Tour 1988–1989

LONDON — Natural History Museum
Cromwell Road, London SW7 5BD   Tel: 01-589 6323
Friday 21st October 1988–Friday 25th November 1988
Open Monday to Saturday 10.00 a.m. to 6.00 p.m.
Sunday 2.30 p.m. to 6.00 p.m.

PLYMOUTH — Plymouth City Museum & Art Gallery
Drake Circus, Plymouth, Devon PL4 8AJ   Tel: 0752 264878
Friday 2nd December 1988–Friday 6th January 1989
Open Monday to Friday 10.00 a.m to 5.30 p.m.
Saturday 10.00 a.m. to 5.00 p.m. Closed Sundays

HEREFORD — Hereford City Museum & Art Gallery
Broad Street, Hereford HR4 9AU   Tel: 0432 268121 (Ext 207)
Saturday 14th January 1989–Thursday 16th February 1989
Open Tuesday, Wednesday, Friday 10.00 a.m. to 6.00 p.m.
Thursday 10.00 a.m. to 5.00 p.m.
Saturday 10.00 a.m. to 4.00 p.m. Closed Sundays

DERBY — Derby Museums & Art Gallery
The Strand, Derby DE1 1BS   Tel: 0332 293111 (Ext 782)
Friday 24th February 1989–Friday 31st March 1989
Open Tuesday to Saturday 10.00 a.m. to 5.00 p.m.
Closed Sundays and Mondays

EDINBURGH — City Art Centre
2 Market Street, Edinburgh EH1 1DE Tel: 031-225 2424 (Ext 6650)
Friday 7th April 1989–Friday 12th May 1989
Open Monday to Saturday 10.00 a.m. to 6.00 p.m.
Closed Sundays

SCARBOROUGH — Scarborough Art Gallery
The Crescent, Scarborough YO11 2PW   Tel: 0723 374753
Friday 19th May 1989–Friday 23rd June 1989
Open Tuesday to Saturday 10.00 a.m. to 1.00 p.m.
and 2.00 p.m. to 5.00 p.m. Sunday 2.00 p.m. to 5.00 p.m.

BLACKPOOL — Pavilion Piazza
Blackpool Winter Gardens & Opera House,
Church Street, Blackpool FY1 3PL   Tel: 0253 25252
Friday 30th June 1989–Saturday 5th August 1989
Open 7 days 9.00 a.m. to 7.00 p.m.

Galleries, opening times and tour dates subject to alteration

Myself

Him

Eyes move surreptitiously in their sockets.
A shrouded figure passes silently.
Thoughts rise, fall, rise again.
Convection currents of the mind.
A pair of eyes latch on to his body
Like magnets.
My mind spools back over the remembered tapes
Of conversation.
He walks over.
Beautiful sound of his feet,
Tapping in time to my thoughts.

I stare at the blank screen of darkness.
My mind remembers.
Colour in my blood,
I walk through his eyes.
Feelings shine through;
Span my world.

Thoughts move surreptitiously in their mind
A shrouded feeling passes silently.

Marion Scholfield (13)
Bangor, Gwynedd

My head

Near my head lies the world,
My head is like an egg but delicate,
It can be broken easily.

Erika Cottle (7)
Long Credon C. Combined School,
Long Credon, Aylesbury
(Highly commended)

Me

My body is like those used in army training,
only I'm the dummy.
My legs are like bean poles,
thin and fragile!
My feet are like cars,
they don't work in the morning,
and they always break down in the fast lane.

My arms are like wings,
useless on the ground.
My face is like a warthog's rear,
I'd rather not go into details.
My ears are like concorde wings,
they're big and they stick out.
My brains are like a schoolboy's pockets,
full of useless things to fascinate.

Elliot Smith (11)
West Park C.E. Middle School,
Goring-by-Sea, W. Sussex

Faster than thought

I ran, I laughed,
I shouted and I smiled.
Racing in the breeze.
Rosy cheeks
And shining eyes,
Hair flowing out behind me,
Skirt pulling at brambles,
A tearing hand.
Socks around my ankles,
Then lying down in the bristly barley
Scratching my chin.
Catching my breath,
Leaping up and haring away until I reached the
    cottage's white gates.
I think . . .
I wish.
I remember.
As I sit in my wheelchair wondering if I will ever be
    there again.

Rebecca Mockford (12)
Potterne, Devizes, Wilts

Seen from a distance

I stand there, against the fence,
Unashamed.
Why should I be otherwise?
The dirt on my leg is a trophy,
Not a blemish, as it would come to be.
The unbrushed hair is a sign of holidays,
Not carelessness.
The white stomach peeps innocently over
The tight denim shorts:
Another sign of holidays.
That same characteristic will become
A weakness, an object of scorn.
Even then, I was being made respectable.
My nose had been blown,
For it was always dripping.
And I wasn't wearing a jumper,
So that I didn't wipe my nose on the cuffs.
Sister Kate perched beside me,
Like the macaws in the background:
A friend amongst enemies,
For she would not tease me,
No matter what she thought
Of her snivelling, introvert brother.
She was changing, even then.
Her arms drooped,
Her hands almost reaching mine,
Although she was a full head taller.
The T-shirt she wore
Was mine within the year,
And a year later still,
It was in the attic,
Amongst the other outgrown clothes.

No longer do we go to Cornwall
Every summer.
Even if we did,
We wouldn't collect the feathers
From the bird-cages.
The attendants must have wondered
What the sticks and Blu-Tack were for.
Now Cornwall isn't warm enough;
We joined the wildlife of the Camargue
For the sun, last time.
I often wondered if I had something to do with it.
I would fight with the boys
Whose parents let us the cottage.
Now I wouldn't fight;
I know better.
Or I should know better.
Gone is the simple, innocent mind
Of childhood.
Everything must be worked out.
Now there is no black or white,
Just grey.
Nothing's safe anymore;
Photos are to be shunned
For they tell the truth,
The truth about the old you,
That you've been trying to suppress
For years.

James Crawford (13)
The King's School, Canterbury, Kent
(Highly commended)

Swimming

When I go swimming
I like to float on my
back to watch the sky pass by.

Michael Commons (6)
Headington, Oxford

Your life and mine

My love for you will break
This rock,
Send memories crashing through
The ocean's sky.
You'll walk on alone and I will
Find you screaming.
In the wind
Seagulls will swoop
Around our fiery head, calling
For our souls,
And I will touch you warm and silently
At dawn and cry
For what has gone before.

It's been so long since I've seen you.

Joanne Pugh (10)
Northfield Middle School,
South Kirkby, W. Yorks

Me

Do you know who I am?
Look at my face,
I am very noble
Please tie up my lace.

Do you know who I am?
Touch me with your hand,
I am very noble
So don't just idly stand.

Do you know who I am?
Smell me with your nose,
I am very noble
Now can you wash my toes?

Do you know who I am?
Listen to what I say,
I am very noble
So don't just sit and play.

Do you know who I am?
The prettiest ever seen,
I am very noble
I am the mighty Queen.

Yvonne Johnson (10)
Shoreham-by-Sea, W. Sussex

Waiting for a rose
(dedicated to Shelley Page)

He shopping-trolleyed his way
Through the cash-till queue
And handed it to me in a
Waitrose bag.
Crushed
like an unwanted receipt
Of his refrigerated
Affections for me.

Catherine Burkinshaw (16)
Aylesbury, Bucks
(Highly commended)

'Hiding in the Winter Garden', Laura Murdoch (11)

18

Smile!

If someone looks at me
I can't help smiling
It's just the way I feel.
Some people say
I smile too much —
They say my smile's not real.

Smiling's in my nature
Or so I've heard it said.
My friends sometimes
Make fun of me
And call me 'happy-head'.

I'm sorry if my smiling
Makes your face feel sore
But when you start your
Jabbering it makes me
Smile the more.

I average one per minute
I'm no good at looking sour,
I just trundle through
My happy life at
Sixty smiles an hour!

Ellen Jackson (14)
Westbury-on-Trym, Bristol

Rumours

I walk in,
I hear the whispers,
They sound like churning waves,
There are people giggling,
People staring,
With ice-cold eyes,
Piercing.
I ask,
What's up with you lot?
No reply,
Just a black silence,
People still stare,
Is it really true?
You are a laugh.
Are you sure she did it?
Of course she did.
I am an animal,
Trapped in a cage,
Where the bars are words.
Well did you?
I bet she did.
I bet she didn't.
Bet she did.
Now I'm a horse,
People betting on me,
Don't I have any feelings?
Did you?
She's sure to say she didn't.
I turn my back,
I leave the room,
I slam the door.

The staring eyes
I see no more,
The whispers and giggles
I hear no more,
But soon everyone will know,
Those rumours,
Those lies.

Nichola White (12)
Minehead Middle School,
Minehead, Somerset
(Highly commended)

My bad day at swimming

I jump into the pool
I splash and splish and splosh
I wet my mummy through
And she looks at me very cross
She smacks me very hard
And I cry very much
She sends me to get dressed
And go home and play so
I didn't have a very good day today

Rebecca Varnouse (6)
Chapel-en-le-Frith, Stockport

Tidying my bedroom

Scrap paper crumpled up
Dropped carelessly into the basket.
On to the pile falls a miniature tiger
Lost and to be forgotten.
I bend down
And pick up the rubbish.
Suddenly, I feel a pin prick
And my finger starts to bleed.
Out of the basket jumps a tiger
And starts to chase a fly.
I reach out my arm,
The tiny toy jumps on to my hand
No longer plastic, but flesh, and hungry –
Around the room it hurries
Eating everything in sight.
It leaps out of the window.
My room is clean
Not a speck in sight
So out I walk and close the door.

Lauren Wilce (10)
Northmead County Middle School,
Guildford, Surrey

A child's lament

8 pm   Please let me stay
Just 'til this last game is won.
Don't send me to bed
While I'm having such fun.

It's comfortable here
There's a great show on TV.
My eyes are wide open,
Look, can't you see?

I'm happy here,
So just for today
Don't send me to bed
Let me stay, let me stay.

8 am   Please let me stay
The night's gone so fast.
Don't make me get up
'Til my dream has passed.

It's comfortable here
And I'm not yet awake
Just five minutes more
Oh! My poor head does ache.

I'm happy here
Can't I sleep in today?
Don't make me get up
Let me stay, let me stay.

James Leggott (10)
Jesmond, Newcastle-upon-Tyne

My bedroom

. . . And piles of comics scattered across the floor,
And bits of torn paper that missed the bin,
And Lego men that fell off their board,
And cupboard doors standing ajar,
And lots of books in the shape of a ramp,
And bits of broken cars left and forgotten,
And colour posters against a white wall,
And an unmade bed with wrinkled pictures of
    Garfield,
And a broken toy bike that didn't make the jump,
And colourful pictures under a table,
And Lego space men starting a take-off,
And a monorail going round an endless loop to
    nowhere,
And piles of comics scattered across the floor . . .

Stephen Davies (11)
Prebendal School,
Chichester, W. Sussex

New desks – but are they?

We got new desks yesterday.
Or at least the rest of the class did.
Of course I got the one
With the BIG FELT PEN MARK in the middle of it.
I went up and told MISS.
BUT she shooed me away.
I tried to rub it off.
I was so embarrassed.
I thought someone might say
'Oh you got the dirty desk!'

John Serhal (10)
St Joseph's School,
Harlesden, London

Bored

I'm BORED, nothing to do today.
The rain's falling faster and faster.
The rain drips slowly on to our car.
No children can play in the rain, the rain.
No children can play in the rain.
I just have NOTHING to do.

Leonie Park (9)
Moorfield County Junior School,
Bridlington, Humbs

Inward emotion

No tears have I,
And yet I cry,

I mouth no words,
And yet I speak,

I ask for no comfort,
And yet feel the touch

I do not hear,
And yet am deafened,

The view is bleak,
And yet I seek,

I think only death,
And yet I am given life.

Katie Warriner (15)
Bonby, S. Humbs

Betrayal

You said that.
You said those words
when we were both happy,
when the sun was beating down on my face
and the grass was tickling my cheek.
You said that,
and I don't understand
how,
if you said that then,
you can so suddenly change your mind
and look back over your shoulder at me
as you wave goodbye,
and I stand at the door
and watch you go
for the last time,
and try and forget
you said
you loved me,
because I love you.

Rowan Macdonald (13)
Beaminster School,
Beaminster, Dorset

Me and you

I sing, you cry.
I have fun, you whinge.
I laugh, you break my toy.
I cry.

Kate Dempsey (7)
Keele, Staffs
(Highly commended)

'Self Portrait', Mark Toalbott (17)

Elegy

I wish I could.
I wish I could take
Her in my arms and say
'Don't cry'.
I wish I could show that
I care,
Say what I mean,
Love as I do.

When my arms
Hang clumsy,
When my cheeks
Blush deep,
When my eyes
Falter,
Cry for me too.

Katie-Louise Thomas (14)
Chelsfield, Kent

Theatre

I saw a play the critics called touching
It did not touch me
It leapt into my soul and
ripped out every secret I had
It paraded them up and down the aisles
All my black things with banners on
stood onstage and
pointed me out to the world
In my seat I wanted to scream
and jump on to the stage
to wrench my life back from the players.

Imane Massoud (15)
International School of London, London
(Highly commended)

Childhood sweetheart

Once we walked in fine rain
      and your hand
      lingered softly in mine
      with subtle perspiration
      like drops of cold sweat
      on summer-day Coke bottles
You picked dandelion bouquets for me
      that I displayed
      in an old aspirin bottle
      on my dresser
Sometimes Mom asks
      'Whatever happened to him, anyway?'
I tell her I don't know −
      but after rainy nights
      I can still smell the sweetness
      of spring clover
      and the fudge brownies
      your mom made for us
      when we promised to drink our milk
      and eat the bread crusts!

Imane Massoud (15)
International School of London, London

My Family

I took a funny photograph

I took a funny photograph
Of my little sister.
Her tongue was sticking out
And her thumbs were in her ears
Her hair was sticking up like a punk
And her dress was all tatty and ripped.
When I showed it to my mum
She laughed and laughed and laughed.
And then she cried a little and said
'Oh, it is a funny photograph.'

Fiona Daubney (8)
St Andrew School,
Rochester, Kent

Daddy's bath

Daddy splishes and splashes
In the water
And he splashes me.
He's all pink and hairy
And he goes red in the water.
He sponges his back,
He wets his hair,
He looks like a pink whale
As he sinks in the bath.
I like to pour cold water over him,
Then he shouts and shouts
And
      I
           run
                 downstairs,

Crying usually.

Natasha Gammon (6)
Cheslyn Hay, Walsall, W. Midlands
(Highly commended)

Happy families?

I ring the bell,
Then ring it again,
Into the hall comes Auntie Jane,
She flings the door open wide,
She asks us all to come inside.
I hold my breath and count to three,
I know what lies ahead of me,
Uncle Bill is in his chair,
Cousin Bob is over there.
And Dolores and Rich from the US of A
They are also on their way.
Nieces and nephews,
Relatives galore,
Start to pile in through the door.
'Oh, look at her size,'
'Hasn't she grown!'
Uncle Albert is on the phone.
They all start to gossip,
Through photos they flick,
All of a sudden I want to be sick.
Through all the photographs they thumb,
Auntie Mo's got a boil on her bum,
Uncle Cyril's got constipation,
And Auntie Jean's had her operation.
'Tea is ready,' I hear Auntie Jane shout,
And one by one we all file out,
We all eat our tea while Dolores brags,
Cyril complains and Auntie Jean nags.
All I can do is sit and eat,
Rodney complains about his feet,
Little Barney strangles the cat,
And hits the dog with a cricket bat.

Uncle Albert slurps his tea,
And little Margaret wants a wee.
In comes the jelly, I watch it quiver,
John's heart is bad and so is his liver.
Everyone takes their share of the jelly,
Barney spoons ice-cream into the telly,
Sidney eats pickles out of the jar,
Uncle Tom smokes his cigar.
Barney plays with Uncle Bill's bowls,
He gets his fingers stuck in the holes,
Everyone tries to get Barney unstuck,
I'm bored so I read the telephone book.
Auntie Dolores brags away,
'We got some more servants the other day,'
Uncle Bob drinks his beer,
Martha is pregnant again we hear.
Albert does his party piece,
He's a magician he saws up my niece.
The bathroom isn't vacant yet,
It's been quite full since the Crepes Suzette.
The night is coming to an end,
I think I'm going round the bend,
Goodnights are said with hugs and tears,
I'm glad I won't see this lot for another few years.

Joanne Potter (14)
Upton, Widnes, Cheshire

Aunt Sue

Her eyes, a meadow green,
Sparkle as she works
endlessly.

Her long, wind-blown brown hair,
Tied loosely in a bow.
Her boots clotted with mud and muck,
The house,
With mixed smells
Of dogs and leather.
Clothes worn,
But her face hard and new.
Hands like a man's,
For she works non-stop.
At home her temper is short,
Yet with her horses,
Her voice is soothing
and calm,
She is a wonder
My Aunt Sue.

Kelly Brown (11)
St Mary's R.C. Junior School,
Gillingham, Kent

Carnivorous water

My sister, balancing her
petite little feet
on the lock traversing the canal;
My . . . paternal? anxiety
as she mockingly feigns a
fatal slip,
my helplessness as she is
muffled by the hardly-translucent
carnivorous water.
Her life flashes before *my* eyes
as the water in the lock forces her
down, down the aged, encrusted
canal banks,
and the ridicule I
put myself through as the trance snaps
and she makes
the last jump on to the
other bank.

Simon Wales (15)
Lichfield, Stockport, Cheshire
(Highly commended)

Visitors

People are coming to stay.
You can tell.
Mum's putting the toys back in their box,
moving the dolls' cot by the window.

I hate it when visitors come.

She's checking the dinner, chicken and trifle;
she's putting her new dress on;
the doorbell rings.

Any second now I'll hear

Hello, darling!
My! How you've grown.

Rachel Hodges (11)
Tupton Hall Schoool,
Chesterfield, Derbys

Nana

Her face and hands are like
Old Autumn leaves.
She delicately picks up a cigarette
and puts it in her mouth like
a life from a cliff.
The life is lit by a match
And smoked away.
Her mouth is a constant chewing motion
Rolling round like cogs.
Her face is the colour of tea stain
And her glasses are like a layer of ice
over her eyes.
They are two windows reflecting
But when she takes them off
Each eye shrinks like
a snail going into a shell.

Kelly Smith (11)
Halesworth Middle School
Halesworth, Suffolk
(Highly commended)

'Grandad', Tom Metcalfe (7)

Granny Ivy

She sits in her chair,
filling it up.
Her hands quickly moving,
The knitting needles clicking together
like the tick of a clock.
The tips of her fingers crumpled,
as if she had stayed in a bath too long,
Press hard against the needles,
Making dents in her marshmallow skin.

Occasionally she pauses,
bends over and pulls at the ribbed,
round ball of wool.
Then back at it again,
in a world of her own.
Her wool world, needle world,
busy knitting the sea.

An ocean of stitches falls over her lap
and tumbles helplessly on the carpet.
Slowly bending forward,
She sticks out her hand,
and gently picks it up.

The piece of knitting with its needles pulled out
looks like a piece of grazed skin,
limp and lifeless.
As she picks up the stitches,
One by one,
She heaves a tired, worn-out sigh,
but smiles lovingly too.

Kirsty Butcher (11)
Halesworth Middle School,
Halesworth, Suffolk

Grandmother

The bright needles clicked;
The old woman's hands,
Quick, dextrous and expert,
Were a blur of colour.
'Your new gloves are finished.'
She eased them on to
My short plump fingers.
'Now you can play in the snow.'
I ran into the street, excited.
The gloves, soft, warm and dry
Were a magical source
Of safety and love.
Time drew on;
My winters grew colder;
The snow fell thicker.
Today my gloves
Are faded and thread-bare;
Her needles lie silent
And my hands are so cold.

Robert McGregor (15)
Debenham High School,
Stowmarket, Suffolk
(Highly commended)

My Grandad

Lives a long way away so I don't see him much.
But when I do he hugs me very hard and laughs.
Just after lunch he has a nap.
Slumped in his chair he snores softly.
A slight smile on his face.
Every morning he makes a cup of tea for my nan.
He feeds the birds.
A hunched figure in the fresh morning air.

Jessica Walter (11)
Darrick Wood Secondary School,
Orpington, Kent

The baby

Quietly I'm playing,
When I hear a noise,
Going thump, thump,
When I peer out I
Get a shock, it is my baby
Brother!
Hastily I retreat,
Trying to find a hiding
Place. I hear him
Drawing near.
Then I hear his battle
Cry 'Ugoo!'
Bravely I take him
Downstairs,
Then I put him in
The lounge.

Christopher Edwards (8)
Radyr, Cardiff

Tea-time

'When is it time for tea, mum?'
'Not yet.'
'I'll go and watch TV then.'
'OK.'
'When is it time for tea, mum?'
'Not yet.'
'I'll go to play at Billy's, then.'
'OK.'
'When is it time for tea, mum?'
'Not yet.'
'I'll go to ride my bike, then.'
'OK.'
'It's tea time!'
'I'm not hungry.'

Paula Digby (11)
St Andrew's
C.E. Primary School,
North Weald, Epping,
Essex

Third time lucky

I am now adopted for the third time;
Third time lucky they always say.
Maybe this adoption will bring me luck —
For my first adoptive parents I was too lazy.
For my second adoptive parents I was too fat.
For my third parents I might be just right.

I stand alone in my room staring at the ceiling,
I look around, everything seems just right.
The room looks expensive
The parents can't really be rich
If they were I definitely wouldn't be here.

My so-called parents keep staring at me;
Maybe they're wondering
'What have we adopted?'
My new mother says
'Don't touch the iron, it's hot.'
I know, I am fourteen, I say to myself.

My new father says
'Don't talk to strangers.'
I say to myself
I am already talking to strangers.

Pavandeep Lochab (13)
Cranford Community School,
Cranford, Middx

My brother

I have a messy brother.
He hid my lunch box.
He eats like a pig.
He puts his rice in his cup
And then puts it back in his bowl.
Then he eats with his fingers.
When he goes to bed
He takes off all his blankets.
But then he's only one.

Hannah Clark (7)
St Johns R.C. First School,
Norwich, Norfolk

Reflections

I see my sister,
Upside down
Walking along a thin wall.
I pick up a stone
And try to knock her down,
But she swallows the stone
And carries on walking,
Swaying slightly from side to side.
Her straight hair is permed
In this wavering watery world.
Her hair is laced with weeds
But a slight breeze
Makes her head shake
And they slowly float away.

Under the surface, fish swim
In and out of my thoughts
And on the floor of the lake
Crabs scuttle
Through the shadows of floating debris.

Jennifer Woolnough (12)
Halesworth Middle School,
Halesworth, Suffolk

My dad left home

It was like a piece of wood
with a small chip in the side,
growing bigger and bigger
as the days progressed
until there's nothing left
and no way to rebuild.

Richard Melody (14)
Sileby, Leics

'Our Basset Hound', Lorna Haskey (13)

My grandpa

I only remember one grandpa,
and I was too young to think him old,
he tried to keep up with me as I grew,
It's hard to climb trees at seventy-three.

Somehow I never gave him up though,
he was my private addiction,
how did it work,
seems impossible to me, but yet it did.

Seemed like the fun only lasted a day,
he gave up his time to me,
walking in the fields with the dog,
he was a man who needed his hands,
　　　　a painter,
　　　　a woodworker.

He also gave me things,
the best an RAF cap,
which brings my memories back,
I grin when I think of him.

Jonathan Dear (12)
Simonballe School,
Hertford

People

A Shetland prayer

Thankdee lorde fur da sun an raen dat maks da
tatties, neeps an a da veegetebles dat grow.
An keeps wis lifen. An da fish wir faders cetch an
da ots da crofters grow fur da oneemals
dat gees wis milk on mit a thankdee lorde
fur da plants dat maks wir yeards a bonny.

This is Shetland dialect. Here is the translation:

Thank you Lord for the sun and rain
that makes the potatoes, turnips and
all the vegetables that grow
and keeps us living.
And the fish our fathers catch
and the oats the crofters grow for
the animals
that give us milk and meat.
I thank you Lord for the plants
That make our gardens beautiful.

Janine Riley (9)
Hamnavoe School,
Burra Isle, Shetland

Born — Norma Jeane

You were a delicate butterfly
Balanced on the end of the human precipice
They pushed you so discreetly
That they didn't even realize they'd done it.
You thought they'd brought you to safety
But you were still teetering on the edge
Slowly, cleverly they changed you
Hairstyle — clothes — name — LIFE.
They manoeuvred you into the most
Vulnerable position of your career
And created the dumb blonde.
They made you dependent on the people around
    you
So that when they turned and slapped you in the
    face
You became dependent on pills.
They didn't expect you to jump over
Just to catch you and be thanked for it eternally
But they fought back after you played your last
    joker
For now we are told of your mental problems
And they have come to analyze your death
Feeling they must explain it in some way.
Then they wrote books and sold them to the world
Sold you — Marilyn.

Frances Graham (13)
Alice Ottley School,
Worcester

Stockbroker

Like a swivel chair,
From nine to five,
A black Monday,
A sly cat, eyeing the market.

Hannah Bayman (10)
West Jesmond Junior School,
Jesmond,
Newcastle-upon-Tyne

What is a tramp?

I see a goose.
I see a man.
I see a hat on the head of the man.
I see grass underneath him.

He is wearing a green jacket,
This man is — this man is,
with yellow patches on each side
One blue patch on one knee.

This tramp — this tramp
he gets up and walks on the cobblestones.
He has one patch on his back.

He goes down to the river
and sits down at the edge
He gets into the river,
He swims away.

Tamasine Johnson (5)
Sheffield

Thoughts from a dentist's waiting room

Please let there be a powercut.
Just a tiny little one.
Just before he gets the drill near my mouth.

One down, two to go

Or maybe he'll be struck down,
By a hitherto undiscovered and as yet incurable
palsy
which only lasts for the ten minutes I'm with him,
and then vanishes forever?

Two down, one to go

Maybe he got the notes mixed up.
'Ridiculous,' he'll say, 'You don't need fillings at all!'
'They're old Mrs Crabtree's notes!' (even though
she has dentures).

NEXT PLEASE!

Why is the dentist the only one who is ever smiling?

Amanda Evans (14)
Enniskillen Collegiate Grammar School,
Enniskillen, N. Ireland

She was never the same

She was never the same after the funeral,
No, never.
She may still have laughed and smiled,
But deep down I knew she cried and grieved.
Oh yes, people felt sorry for her, but no one really
    cared.
No, no one really cared.
In front of her face her 'friends' sorrowed,
However, when it was turned, they mocked.
She was never the same after the funeral.
Never.
Now there was no one, not a shoulder to cry on,
No one to trust or to care for her,
No one to care for.
Especially herself.
No, she was never the same after the funeral.

Andrew Bogan (12)
Gosforth Central Middle School,
Gosforth, Newcastle-upon-Tyne

Unwanted life

The red door opened.
In he stepped.
A hard day's work
Made no image
On an iron face.
His solitary plate lay,
Lukewarm upon the wooden table;
The food tasted bitter.
Bitter as the hands
That had prepared it.
He 'retired' to the library.

She sat, sewing in the lounge,
The shirt being undone
For the fifth time.
Red blood spots clotted
Unnoticed, on the end
Of clumsy fingers.
The chandelier produced an unwilling light
Without a flicker of attention.
Unwantedness broke her.
A pin prick,
A silent yelp,
Then her face disintegrated
Behind a cascade of salty water.
Tears of self-pity.

A little girl,
Trapped between
Her parents' anger,
Bounced to and fro
Like a tennis ball.
After the fifth game
The balls were changed.
She scuttled up to her room
And ripped a staring,
Innocent doll in two.
Falling on to her cold bed,
She cried tears of bafflement.

In the library
He read the same line
Ten times, then again,
But in vain, for the words
Could not penetrate his glazed eyes.
He put the book
And his superficial face
Down.
Tears stained the tablecloth.
Tears of guilt.

The house still stood.
The red door lay open,
A cat sat, unperturbed.
The walls were made of grief, pity, sorrow.
The young girl buried
Her head in a soaking pillow.
A pool of rejection,
Of unwanted life.

Richard Gipps (13)
The King's School,
Canterbury, Kent

The ageing year

A middle-aged man grows older.
Crew-cut of hollow stubble
Frozen ground of muscle.
Heavy breath of mist hangs
Eyes of dew glisten in the low-slung sun
Trees stretch bare, bony hands.
Leaves are deep red of his cheeks caught by sun
As his time runs fast so day ends quickly.

Michelle Carter (11)
Lostock Gralam Primary School,
Lostock Gralam, Cheshire

'Old Master', Peter Kelly (17)
(Italian Tour Award winner)

Trapeze Artist

A sea of smiling faces
Waves dizzily below.
The sawdust appears, uncertainly
For half a second.
Someone's glittering costume
Looms before her . . .
She grabs it.
The mouths below cheer.
Limbs entwined,
She swings to the safety
Of a creaking, wooden parapet —
Flushed red, but
Smiling.

Kate Quinn (12)
Claudy, Londonderry, N. Ireland

'We, the residents'

Part 1

Dear Councillor,
      It's nearly June, you know, and We —
      (The local residents)
      Have found that shared amongst our ranks
      Is mutual discontent:
      Behind our row of five-bed homes
      (Built by Regent-Loch)
      Is a farmyard which is owned by
      A man of 'dubious stock'.
      Now naturally, I would *hate*
      To cause his family grief —
      And yet the trouble *he* has caused
      Is quite beyond belief!
      To put you in the picture briefly,
      Here's an explanation:
      The animals he keeps are *pigs* —
      They have no sanitation.
      At feeding time they go quite mad,
      The noise they make's horrific!
      They go on squealing all day long . . .
      (Well, 'til four, to be specific)
      Now, Mrs Rutleigh (No. eight)
      Spoke of you quite highly
      (She said you did a good job
      With that spaniel-owner Riley)
      She mentioned it in passing,
      When you did the Spring Fete plant-stall:
      'Speak to Councillor Jones' she said,
      'She's rather influential.'

(I'm the one who said
The previous Councillor was a failure —
You sold me some silk flowers,
And a beautiful Azalea.)
So as we're near acquaintances
I thought I'd see if you
Could stop this outright blatancy —
(Pull a string or two).
However, now it's in your hands,
I'll return to my jam-making —
A sincere 'thank you' in advance!
(I hope you'll be partaking
Of my famous plum preserve
At this year's County Show?
I'll keep four jam-jars in reserve.)

     Sincerely,
         Mrs Lowe

Part 2

Dear Councillor
    Thanks for writing, councillor
    Or may I call you Beryl?
    But I'm *most* distressed to learn
    That our beloved farm's in peril!
    You may be puzzled slightly
    At my choice of wording here
    But I gather from my writing
    That you got the wrong idea:

My letter (dated late in May)
Has led to a perversion
Of what I really meant to say —
You think I've an aversion
Towards my neighbour, Mr Flint?
— I may have hinted so —
Yet this is not at all the case
(It may interest you to know
That Mr Flint's the chief supplier
Of Lord Hunt's Ham, no less —
We wouldn't want to force his buyer
To serve him second best . . .)
But on to more important things
Concerning our pig-farm:
Amongst the local residents
Is growing some alarm
You see, your letter (just received)
— I *know* it's confidential —
(And though it's hard, you must believe
That I was *most* prudential)
But Martha Mary Ardenshaw —
She 'does' for me twice-weekly —
Found it in my Bureau
And came to me quite meekly:
Confessing that she'd told her friends,
Who live down Stavely Walk
(Well, you know how these char-women
    are,
And how their neighbours talk)
It's escalated, Mrs Jones
And some are quite irate:
Destroy a haven of green space
For a new *council* estate!
We know you have to listen to

Those of lower breeding
But talk to the town-planning man –
Do stop him from conceding!
If we give in to people
Who these council homes are for
They'll never save themselves from staying
'Working Class', and poor.
I *love* green spaces (as must you)
And would hate it if they filled them
With single-parent families,
And spray-can bearing children!
One may think that pig-farms
Are a penny for a dozen
But I'm assured the contrary
By a cattle-owning cousin.
To this effect, I've made myself
Chairman of a committee:
'Protect Historic Pig-farms!' –
They are disappearing quickly!
And since you are acquainted with
The facts of our 'Pork Heritage'
We'd like you to be president
(We'd feel it such a privilege)
Please reply, as soon as poss –
These men are far from slow:
The land surveyor's just arrived!

    Sincerely,
       Mrs Lowe

Kathryn Boydell (15)
Priestnall Comprehensive School,
Heaton Mersey, Stockport
(Highly commended)

Untitled

She stood there with her hands clenched,
nails digging into her palms like daggers.
The colour rose on her cheekbones
searing like fever across her skin,
'I hate you!' she screamed.
Slam! went the door
and then the sound of her heels clicking on stone
    steps,
the muffled bang as she stormed out of the house.
Not caring about traffic, she ran across the road,
the sudden screech of wheels and she was caught,
like a deer,
in the headlights.
The quickly-turned head,
eyes glinting like a gypsy,
was the one impression the driver caught before he
    swore at her
and jammed the steering wheel over to avoid her.

She reached the river,
fumbling with the silver circle on her left hand,
she was about to fling it angrily across the water,
but she stopped
and let the tears fall down her face like sheets of
    water.

When her anger cooled,
she held the ring high above the surface
and let it drop.
It fell with a small chink
like ice cubes falling into lemonade.

Rowan Macdonald (13)
Beaminster School,
Beaminster, Dorset

The accused

The old man hangs his head in shame,
Was not his fault, is not to blame.
Doctors surrounding, sterilizing,
Ending all his fantasizing.
The typewriter burnt upon the pyre,
Pens and pencils whipped by fire.
Paper gloriously set alight
And is destroyed without a fight.
The government warning went unheeded,
Some drastic action then was needed.
Imagination has no place
In this computer-age-of-space.
Books abandoned, poems burnt,
The lesson has not yet been learnt.
Later, when he's locked away,
Shut in his padded cell all day,
The guilty admits his only crime —
Imagination, tales and rhyme.

Deborah Parkin (14)
Duffield, Derby

Elderly man

When she died
I didn't do the figures,
For I haven't the head
For such things.
They sent red letters through the door,
Demanding their money,
Always wanting more.
But I was so confused.
And in the end angry men
Came, took away my things
And then,
They came and took me.
'Didn't the neighbours ever pop in?
All on your own,
You poor old thing!'
They made it alright.
'There's quite a nice place
Near to here.
Why the sulky face?'
I was stupid to them,
Just another case,
An elderly man
To feed, to place.
Tuck me away.
My house, my kids, my Beth,
Held us in Life
But not so now in Death.
It's no longer mine.
They never found the key.
It was all changed
When I went back to see,
I died inside.

Helen Goff (14)
Uxbridge, Middx

64

It was herd work but

It was herd work but
De wid dance and sing fir a ours o di night.
And den de wid gay'n lie on a stra mattres.
Den in di morning de wid bendege up dir
fingers an start gutting.
Den a nider wife wid pak it.
Di coppers made barrels fir di hirring.

This is written in Shetland dialect about the 'Herring Gutters in Scotland'. Here is the translation:

It was hard work but . . .
They would dance and sing for all hours of the
    night.
And then they would go and lie on a straw
    mattress.
Then in the morning they would bandage
up their fingers and start cutting.
Then another woman would pack it.
The coopers made barrels for the herring.

Ellis Halcrow (9)
Hamnavoe School,
Burra Isle, Shetland

There is a smudge of bad in all of us

There is a smudge of bad in all of us,
Something that is there deep inside,
Nagging a space for itself,
Something that can't be dug out with a spade,
Knocked out with a hammer,
Threatened out with fire.
But it's there
And it flavours whatever we do.

Michael Duggan (12)
Beckenham, Kent

'The Swimming Pool', Sarah Gallway (18)
(Italian Tour Award winner)

Reflection

The old man sits
By the river
Reflecting.
The river is still
Until
A raindrop
Pierces its surface
Like a needle.
No needle
Can repair
The cushion he made
To protect
His family
Now the stitching
Is rent
And
The contents spilled.
His moist eyes see
A line
As fine
As thread.
Rough hands reach out
But
The needle has rusted;
The pin has tarnished;
The thread has strained.
The pin drops
But
The old man
Does not hear.

Clare Smith (15)
Debenham High School,
Stowmarket, Suffolk

Sue

In control of her viewers,
She sits like a queen;
Calm, collected, expressionless.
Her speech is flawless,
Her hair perfect.

She announces coldly the desolate streets,
The total destruction
In the aftermath of the huge hurricane.
She states in her full tone
That yet another famine has struck.
As we see dead corpses strewn like litter,
We cry.
Yet not a sigh does she heave,
Not a tear does she shed.

The most important person for thirty minutes —
We feel at one with her,
Despite her designer outfits.
Every cue, every pause — on time.
Nothing can go wrong;
Nothing does go wrong — ever.

Sharon Foy (17)
Lourdes Secondary School,
Glasgow

The man on the beach

Fat beer belly
Hanky on head,
He sits in the sun
Back going red.

Sprawled in a deckchair
Watching the tide,
In purple trunks
Beer at one side.

No time to care
No time to worry,
He just sits there
Not having to hurry.

The tide creeps around him,
The waves kick up foam,
He picks up his paper
Time to go home!

Lisa Sanderson (13)
Headlands School,
Bridlington, Humbs

Full house

The old lady
Across our street
Has only two things
That keep her alive —
Her Marlboros and
Bingo.
It's the same
Each Friday night.
She opens her door,
7.30 sharp.
With her grey mac
and purple hat.
In her eyes
A look of eagerness,
As if waiting
For the starter's gun.
Then, not so sharp
The taxi
Forever,
A Ford,
Yellow.
In she gets.
Looks around.
Then off,
Into the night.
There she sits
In the hall.
Card at the ready.
Her old, arthritic hands
Nervously shaking,
But nimbly moving.

As the young man,
In blue suit and tie,
Picks the numbers.
The old lady,
At wit's end
As the numbers are called,
Come over the loudspeaker.
The card
Filling up.
Her heart
Full, of
Anticipation.
Eyes the numbers quickly.
Clears her throat.
The card
Fills up,
Then,
Out of the blue
'Bingo'
From the other side of the hall.
The night's work over.
She returns,
Defeated.
Yet still,
Each Friday,
The same.
She has a massive house.
Just her on her own.
Even though she tries,
She'll never get
Her dream.
A Full House.

Nathanael Selman (11)
Exeter, Devon
(Highly commended)

'The King George',
Jane Elizabeth Pursey
(14)

It was herd work but . . .

Tie your fingers een efter da ither
Hurry noo, boats oh na time ta dither.
Wirk, wirk, wirk a da time
If only dis herrin wisna sticky as slime.
Rasmie's cumin roond t'night
Between dee an me he's no very bright
He's tik as twa planks
He's daft as a table
If only he looked like handsome Clark Gable.
OWCH!
I've cut my han an it's na half sair
It's wer as when I locked me finger in da door.
A herd day's wark is ower at last
An am got a sore head
So I tink I'll wander hame tae bed.

This poem is in Shetland dialect. This is the translation:

Tie your fingers one after the other
Hurry now, boats, oh no time to dither.
Work, work, work all the time
If only this herring wasn't sticky as slime.
Rasmie's coming round tonight
Between you and me he's not very bright
He's thick as two planks
He's daft as a table
If only he looked like handsome Clark Gable.
OWCH!
I've cut my hand and it's not half sore
It's worse as when I locked my finger in the door.
A hard day's work is over at last
And I've got a sore head
So I think I'll wander home to bed.

Peter Ratter (9)
Hamnavoe School,
Burra Isle, Shetland

Animals

My secret world

Muddy and mossy
You won't find my secret world.
Specks of sunlight
Evenly cast shadows
Crispy leaves
Red, brown and gold
Evening draws near
The shadows grow longer
Wind moans
On the horizon the sun sets
Rats forage
Leaves rustle
Down in the hedge bottom.

Richard Gregory (7)
Norwell C.E. Primary School,
Norwell, Notts

If I was a rabbit

If I was a rabbit,
I wouldn't have the habit
of twitching my nose up and down.
I'd just laze about
relaxing my snout,
and cleaning my coat of brown.

If I was a rabbit,
I wouldn't have the habit
of eating carrots and greens.
I'd have ice cream and jelly
to fill up my belly,
with chocolate chips and beans.

If I was a rabbit,
I wouldn't have the habit
of living underground.
I'd live up in a tree
for all to see,
and watch the world go round.

If I was a rabbit,
I'd love the habit
of romping around and free.
But dangers abound
for all above ground —
so just for now I'll be me!

Stephanie Amos (11)
St Anne's C.E. Middle School,
Bewdley, Worcs

The fish

The fish glimmers as it swims swiftly,
It is stunning and elegant as it moves slowly and
   lazily along the bed.
Powerfully it struggles upstream
With the strength of an ox.

It has wide eyes like those of a rabbit,
The light catches the scales of the fish
As it dives to find food,
And hovers along the bottom.

After feeding it swims off silently
As though not to waken any predators,
The fish dives, twists and tosses
As it wriggles upstream.

Settling into a calm river,
Now the strength has been drained.
It stays in one place lifeless,
As if hanging from a string.

Christopher Haskins (12)
Tockington Manor School,
Tockington, Bristol

The river king

The surface of the river
is broken.
A v-shaped ripple
moves along.
Like an eddy
it pauses.

Slowly a small furry head
appears by the bank.
Silence – all is well.
Two bright eyes survey the scene,
The water vole emerges.
His fur glints like silver in the sunshine.
As he reaches for
his breakfast of
tasty reed.
His hunger satisfied,
he meditates.
Like a furry potentate,
The bank his throne.
The river is his kingdom.
But wait,
The jay calls a warning,
Footsteps approach.
The silence is broken.
Plop!
He is king no more.
Only glistening bubbles
Betray his presence
as he glides through the water
to his home underground.
Safe once more.

Anna Mignot (11)
Fernhill Manor Junior School,
New Milton, Hants

The cat parrot

There's not a mouse in all the house.
Of that I can be sure.
The other day
We found a way to drive them from the door.
They lived up in the attic
But don't go near it now
Since father brought a parrot and taught it to
    meeow.

Katherine Grinnell (7)
Abbey Junior School,
Sandwell, W. Midlands
(Highly commended)

———

Slugs

Slugs
Splodgy softness
Slowly they move
Little shiny black bulldozers
Slugs.

Benjamin Mann (9)
Northmead County
Middle School,
Guildford, Surrey

King of the alley

A young girl, and a pretty kitten
Rolling among wrapping paper.
An old tom, scarred head held erect,
Exiled on a dustbin.
A lord with dwindling kingdom,
A king without a crown.
But still a lord, and still his
Worn down claws prove lethal
To the rats who are now his only subjects.
Older in years than the number of
Kittens his many wives have borne.
His castle a cardboard box,
His kitchen a restaurant's open window.
The old monarch sleeps
Among piles of newspaper.

Sarah Smith (11)
Alltwen, Swansea, Glamorgan

The cow

Did you see me?
Did you watch me
Lumbering on cracked hooves
Round the shed?
Did you see my spine hump up
As I leaned forward
And smelled for grass in the faded straw. . . ?

My skin shimmering to
Flick away flies?
Did you see my face?
My gentle brown eyes,
Mysteriously holding back a secret.
My nose,
Shaped like an oversize strawberry,
Black with a splotch of dull pink,
And covered in droplets of water,
My nostrils,
Opening and closing
Like sea-anemones.

My tail,
A seaman's frayed rope,
Well used.
My ears,
Curled leaves protruding from my head,
Flicking round to catch sound
Of your first whimper . . .
Did you see?

Lara Mair (12)
Halesworth Middle School,
Halesworth, Suffolk
(Arthur Lines Poetry Award winner)

The cat

The cat slowly emerged from behind the bush,
   piece by piece,
Two eyes peered hungrily,
Its ears were pricked upright eagerly listening out
   for food,
Cautiously he stepped out,
He scanned the empty lawn, not a bird in sight,
Then a blackbird flew down and hopped about
   inquisitively,
Not aware of its enemy,
The cat grinned and his white teeth gleamed,
He lowered himself, wiggled and prowled across
   the grass, silently,
Getting nearer and nearer, his heart pounding,
His tail down low,
Stretching his claws out wide, he crouched and
   then pounced like lightning on the poor creature,
   as if it were a ball of wool,
Tearing, scraping, biting, gnawing rapidly it flung
   the ragged creature around,
Scattered about the lawn, pieces of a demolished
   bird could be seen,
The cat slunk away leaving its prey.

Rachel Holmes (11)
Newstead Wood School,
Orpington, Kent

A mouse lived in a laboratory

The scientists dyed a mouse bright blue
To see what all its friends would do.
Its friends, they didn't seem to mind . . .
The scientists wrote down their find.

The scientists cut the mouse's brain
To see if it would act the same.
The mouse was still able to think . . .
The scientists wrote this down, in ink.

The scientists took the mouse's brain
Clumsily sewed it up again.
The mouse, it acted like a clown . . .
The scientists wrote all this down.

The scientists tied the mouse's feet
And buried it in soil and peat
The mouse quite liked it in the muck . . .
The scientists wrote this in their book.

Soon afterwards the scientists tried
To spin the mouse until it died.
The mouse loved whirring round and round . . .
(The scientists' pad was spiral bound.)

The mouse, by now immune to pain
Could not have been of use again.
Red cross through notes, and 'Mouse no good' . . .
The scientists wrote this down.
In blood.

Kathryn Boydell (15)
Heaton Norris, Stockport, Cheshire

Stick insect

It is in a jungle of privets,
Body swaying side to side.
Put on my hand, it is barely felt.
Its pale skin a green illusion,
Its waving antennae feel the air.

Michelle Seager (11)
Ellen Wilkinson High School,
Ardwick, Manchester

'Buffalo', James Smith (10)

Grasshopper

Mechanical digger legs puff up the dust.
His head, a peach stone, but green, with two deep
   black eyes.
Behind his head metal armour protects his delicate
   insides.
His back is a cigar with pointed green leaves
   carefully folded over.
The jumping is graceful, quick to the eye.
A flick of the leg and he is gone.

Joe Ward (11)
Halesworth Middle School,
Halesworth, Suffolk

The spider

In her web the spider lies,
Waiting for a horde of flies.
Thread of finest silk she wove,
Right beside the kitchen stove.
Working with her spinnerets,
The thread came out in silver jets,
To make a patterned lacy cap,
That really was an awful trap
For any unsuspecting fly
That happened to be buzzing by!

Lee Holloway (10)
Michael Drayton Middle School,
Hartshill, Nuneaton, Warwicks

My cat

When my cat's asleep and lying on my bed
I wonder what she dreams of in her little head.
Her whiskers start twitching
her paws start to shake
her tail starts thrashing
its a wonder she doesn't wake.
Perhaps she dreams of birds and mice
or a juicy big fat rat
or how to escape from Podger our other skinny cat.
Perhaps she dreams of seas of cream
or delicate chicken livers
huge sides of beef and shoals of fish.
Maybe that's why her nose quivers
with a stretch and a yawn
she looks at me then
jumps down on the mat and waits patiently
while she watches me open a tin of kitty kat.

David Woodrow (9)
Market Bosworth C.E. Primary School,
Market Bosworth, Warwicks

The snail

At daybreak the Alien Snail appears.
He stretches out like a piece of chewing gum.
Down his spiral staircase shell he comes
from his bedroom.
His tentacles pop out like car aerials.
He slips and slides along the dirty path
Trying to find fresh succulent leaves.
Behind him he leaves a meandering trail.
On finding a leaf he chomps away, leaving
    a ragged hole.
Carrying his home on his back
He travels through the darkness of the
night until he finds a cool dark place
to shelter until daybreak.

Lee Root (9)
Wimborne Middle School,
Portsmouth, Hants

The lizard

Something on the wall
Is perched quite still,
Except for the throbbing of its sides.
Something on the wall
Will stay still, or it will
Shoot up (or down) very fast.

Something on the wall
Is camouflaged well,
And when it is startled moves away.
Something on the wall
Is a decimetre small,
And sometimes stays for a day.

Catherine Smart (11)
London
(Highly commended)

It was this?

It was this
when it was young.

It had changed over
a few weeks.

Soon she will be having
chicks of the sun.

They will be like
cold white pebbles.

Then a smashing glass
cracks open.

As she fluffs up
it is like the sun rising.

Joanne Jennings (12)
St Mary's Gate School,
Southbourne, Dorset

Dog dozes

Curled up.
Crouched, like a muffin
In front of the fire,
To toast.

Electric glow
Darts her eyes.
Heat absorbed,
Cold light flashed back.

Nose on wrist
She ponders.
Eyes close.
Her mind slinks away.

Helen Rahman (14)
Chorley, Lancs

Born still

It is cold;
the slanting rays of the moon
penetrate the broken glass of the shed window.

The only noise is the strangled bleating
of a new born lamb,
hobbling on its gangly legs,
trying to reach its mother's milk.

The other has a silent bleat.

It does not move
but lies there, still as a stone.

It is wrapped in a white blanket,
a baby's blanket.

It left as soon as it came.
I lift it into my arms.
I do not cry. There are no tears to spill.

I carry it away to rest someplace else.

Fiona Boulding (12)
Tupton Hall School,
Chesterfield, Derbys

'Mowgli and Sher Khan', Stephen Callaghan (6)
(Highly commended)

The snail

Leaving behind me my trade mark,
My slippery, shiny trail,
A permanent removal van,
Never unpacked,
My house, a twisting pebble colour,
Security from those giant feathery beasts,
My neck cranes forward, reaching for nothing,
Sliding back into my house,
Cautiously peeping out towards the ground,
I travel at my leisure,
Nice and slowly,
Some would call me pessimistic,
I would say happy,
Scared but happy.

Jennifer Brown (12)
Sidcot School,
Winscombe, Bristol

Perseverance of a spider

Climbing up the slimy slide,
One way to go, nowhere to hide.

Then comes the rumbling water increasing,
Round the corner almost cascading,
Hitting me hard then dragging me down,
To end in the sewers under the town.

Swirling, diving, dipping and spluttering,
Down the shute into the guttering.
There I rest in my watery tomb,
To start up again to the warm bathroom.

I'm climbing up the bathroom walls,
Learnt my lesson, no more falls.

Caroline Lusher (13)
St Martin's School,
Solihull, W. Midlands

The spider in the manger

Sitting in her silver palace,
The spider queen looks down upon him,
She strains her eyes in the gloom,
But can see only his bright eyes.
She spins a thread and climbs down gently
Yet still she can see only eyes.
Then she falls silently
And unnoticed into the palm
Of a tiny hand.
She scrambles up his arm.
Then stops and looks
At his beautiful thread.
He picks her up in his other hand,
More gently than if it were his mother
Taking him in her hands.
He lifts the queen up to her thread.
Then eyes of queen meet eyes of king
And she knows life has changed.

Alistair Bowrow (13)
The Mountbatten School,
Romsey, Hants

The cat

One day I saw
A cat.
She was
Squabbling
And pouncing
And scratching.
And I said
Stop it!
So she stopped.
And the
Cat said,
Who
Are you?
I am
Lisa.
Do you want to be
My friend?
Yes, said
The
Cat.
So that was
That.

Lisa Betts (7)
Willoughton
County Primary
School,
Willoughton, Lincs

Evening kill

They stare from the bushes.
Two pools of molten gold.
Gleaming, with strong intent.
A black pupil in each fiery pond,
like an eclipsed moon.
Whiskers twitch, sensing the air.
Two deadly weapons,
tucked under motionless chin, always ready.
Black snake lashes impatiently.
Then is still.
A movement in the silver-fronded grass.
A second pair of eyes,
dark as the shadows cast by the sinking sun.
They blink inquisitively.
Not knowing fear.
Silky death bunches itself in the bushes.
Ready to spring.
It quivers, muscles tense.
Then leaps,
famished with the hunger to destroy.
Ten curved scimitars are unleashed
from their white sheath.
A shrill call.
At last fear is recognized.
The ten hooks descend, strike.
A crimson-red river flows.
The end is near.
Black feathers fly.
As if to herald the death.
Coral-like, jagged teeth
close round the dying body
as a tidal wave engulfs a stricken isle.

Its eye takes in its home for the last time.
What has gone wrong with the world?
Then submits, and dies.
Cat drops the drooping victim.
Lies down in the sun.
Closes its blood-lusting eyes.
A deep, continuous throbbing rises,
vibrating its throat.
The last rays of the sun play on the deathly scene.

Heidi Scott (12)
Ayr, Scotland

'Elephant Mother and Baby', Kerry Baker (15)
(Highly commended)

Panther

Springs, full of lissom grace
– sleek ebony ribbon
amongst sackcloth strips
weaving a deadly trail.

Cautious yet sure, with eyes aflame
silently slinks, seeking,
probing, every footstep
a missionary of death.
The prey stands unawares.

A sleek jet sovereign;
raven silk cutting through
coarse grass and jungle heat.
The prey lies unawares.

A quicksilver streak – fangs
gleam an evil scarlet;
razor jaws clasp dead flesh
– the predator skulks away;
The eclipse of man and beast.

Helen Norman (13)
Stourport-on-Severn High School,
Stourport-on-Severn, Worcs

The midnight fox

When the night is young
And is waiting to be used,
To be blown, to be sounded,
The orange fox with moonlight eyes
Prowls,
Snooping, with nostrils quivering
As the wind disturbs quiet smells that hide in the
cloak of the shadows,
And he smiles.

Michael Duggan (12)
Beckenham, Kent

Woodpecker

I am a woodpecker
and my name is Fred.
I live in a tree
where the bark is dead.
I fly through the air
like an aeroplane free
higher and higher
to my favourite tree.

Jonathan Byrne (5)
Cheswycks School,
Frimley Green, Surrey

On fish

I

In the lightless blue
of seas and oceans,
silver splits through
unmoving aqua;
a cold eye stares
unblinkingly at
coloured rocks;
a flash of fun,
and the shoal
vanishes.

II

The nets heap hundreds of fish daily,
thrashing bodies churning brine
in the nylon cage that chokes on sun-touched
    scales.
Unrelenting, they find their way
into supermarkets,
frozen into spineless blocks of ice,
dusted with breadcrumbs
and packed in cardboard;
or displayed on market stalls,
neatly decapitated, intestines removed
and suitably disposed of.
The dead are patient;
uncomplaining, they await sale.

III

Sticky hands clutch proudly
the leaky plastic bags,
inside whose translucent walls
Goldfish
swim monotonously around
and around
and around
Flicking tails at spectators,
conducting carnival music.
Candyfloss is abandoned
at the chance to win
'The Ideal Pet'.

IV

Flash of grey
slices through white water,
sudden snap at a fly
and the form falls back
before it's even seen;
but you know it was a salmon,
as sure as the clammy bodies
fight their race upriver
every year.

V

Someone has filled a whole book
with diseases of fish.
Move over AIDS;
here we have
constipated Goldfish.

VI

Hiss of fishing line;
a far-off splash
and the hook sinks,
metallic
through rush of blue.
A quick flick of hand
and the prize is lifted forth;
careful hands weigh it,
measure it,
slip the hook out
and drop the cold heart
into a wickerwork basket.

VII

A swift plunge;
feathers break the surface,
sending crowns of water
spinning in the air.
One snatch of an open beak
and a trout is stolen
from its river home;
swallowed.
Preparation is made
for the next dive.

VIII

Colours wink through glass walls,
False sunlight falls on foreign bodies.
The tropical fish
brush side by side with pebbles
gathered on Cemlyn.
Electric blues,
sequined greens,
silvered reds
all waltz hypnotically
through showcase oceans.

IX

A smiling fisherman
Clad in waxed jacket,
winner of a competition,
holds up the slain pike
for a camera. The fish,
held by its torn gills,
is framed;
'A good catch for David Ellis'
becomes its epitaph.

Fish (1) (pl. fishes or fish)
[fish] n. cold-blooded
finned vertebrate, living
in water and breathing by gills;
any animal living in water;
flesh of such animal used as food.

Siobhan Aiton (15)
Ysgol Gyfun, Llangefni (Llangefni
Comprehensive School)
Anglesey, Gwynedd
(Italian Tour Award winner)

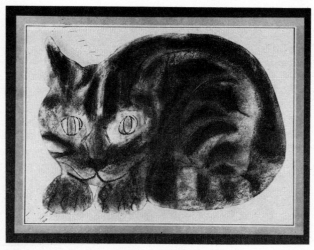

'Cat', Penelope Jane Illingworth (11)

Look, listen, wait . . .

Look, and keep very still,
Still as a tree,
And if you do, you may see,
A black and white badger carrying her young,
Scuffling through the bushes,
Then she cuts across the track,
Hurrying to get home.

Listen, and keep very still,
Still as a tree,
And if you do, you may hear,
A flutter of wings as the owl flies overhead,
Quickly she goes,
She gives a quick hoot and then she is gone.

Wait, and keep very still,
Still as a tree,
And if you do, you may feel,
Beetles scurrying about by your feet,
Wriggling and worming through the leaves,
You move, and they dash for cover.

Carol Shiels (11)
Northmead County Middle School,
Guildford, Surrey

My mouse Chalky

Chalky my pure white mouse
Lived under the roof of my house,
I fed it on sunflower seeds
And it slept on long straw reeds.
Then, on one summer's evening
Dad told me that it was suffering,
Suffering from what we did not know.
But then Chalky died and I was full of sorrow.
I went down to the garden and dug a little pit,
I put Chalky in an envelope and laid him in it.
Then at bedtime I couldn't get to sleep
Chalky was hanging in my mind
And I began to weep.
When I woke up next morning I felt there was
   something wrong,
I remembered little Chalky with his tail so long
And how he died so young in age.
I went at once to the Wallrover cage,
I saw Blacky, Smoky and our two other mice,
But it wasn't the same without Chalky my mouse.

Peter Robbins (7)
St Chad's C.E. Primary School,
Leeds

She called it her robin

She called it her robin.
And once she took me to see.
All she did
Was outstretch her hand
And sprinkle
Cheese crumbs
On the palm.
She would call softly,
'Robby, Robby.'
Nothing happened at first,
But then,
A rose bush
Sprang to life
As her robin,
Wings vibrating,
Flew from his nest in the roots.

He landed, delicately,
On her palm.
His breast was brick red,
The edges a musty orange
Fading into the brown of his back.
His eyes shone,
Chips of wet flints
Smoothed round.
His beak was like the tip
Of a rose thorn
As he pecked for the cheese.

She spoke to him soothingly,
Dragging out the vowel sounds,
'Robby, my little Robby,'
The tip of her little finger
Tracing down his back
As she lovingly stroked
Her fickle friend.

Lara Mair (12)
Halesworth Middle School,
Halesworth, Suffolk
(Arthur Lines Poetry Award winner)

Nature and Seasons

Wind, wind

I don't know where the wind goes.
Nobody knows where the wind goes.
If I let go of my kite
It will know where the wind goes.

Tom Finch (6)
Highfield School,
Highgate, London

Here we go again

Here we go again,
Problems with the rain.
We look around,
We've got wet ground,
Here we go again.

Julian Yon (7)
Cleethorpes, S. Humbs

Earth Child

Born of earth,
this brittle child of clay
baked by the sun kiln;
a thin figure rolled in mud,
fired in blistering heat,
this earth child, son of
rainless desert,
dust-child, shell-spattered.

Only in his eyes
is the soil moist;
and here it is stolen
by flies that crawl
like thieves
across the cracked chasm
of lips that bleed air.

Feed him rain;
Let his parchment-thin body
soak up liquid, breathe water.

Soften the cracked clay.

Siobhan Aiton (15)
Ysgol Gyfun, Llangefni (Llangefni
Comprehensive School)
Anglesey, Gwynedd
(Italian Tour Award winner)

The snow queen

The Snow Queen dazzling white
Rides on a white sledge pulled by swans
When she comes she throws snowflakes behind her
      Her snowflakes fall like feathers
      She lives in the North Pole
A magic cloak flies behind her
      She leaves crystals on the trees
A crown of icicles on her head.
She throws a blanket of white on the ground.
The first light of dawn shows
back to the North Pole she flies
      back to her ice palace
      Her battlements shine
Her sentries guarding the palace from sunbeams
      We wake to a blanket of white
Saying the Snow Queen has been.

Joanne Birch (7)
Marston Green Junior School,
Marston Green, Birmingham

Salt-lake Cyprus

The flamingoes dazzled by the sun
A lake of pink confetti
The huge dull salt trucks
Shimmer in the heat
The tiny grains of salt
As glittery as diamonds
When the trucks are filled to the top
They rumble away
Salt sticking in the gloomy black tyres
The birds fly to the sky
Like pink gliders
Slipping away into the stretch of blue.

Samantha Budworth (11)
St Mary's Gate School,
Southbourne, Dorset
(Highly commended)

The wind

The wind is swooping through the trees
And blowing all the clouds.
I am playing with my kite
Flying over the tree tops.

The wind is whizzing round and round.
It's howling like a wolf.
It sounds like the waves crashing
And bashing the clouds together.

The trees are begging.
The trees are bowing.
The trees are waving their arms.

Group Work (5/6)
Gaer Infant School,
Newport, Gwent

'Landscape with Cows', Nicola Flockart (16)

Whose season?

The sleek red fox
Creeps through the night.
He's alert, nimble and cautious,
Hunting down his dinner.
But he, too, is hunted.
Winter is not the season
Of the sleek, red fox.

The sheep looks fit for winter,
His thick woollen coat serves him well,
But he still huddles close to his companions,
To keep the cold at bay.
The grass is sprinkled with frost,
Making grazing quite impossible.
Winter is not the season
Of the sheep.

As winter presses on
The cheeky red squirrel sleeps,
But on a mild December day
He'll awake for a snack, scrabbled
From his storage jar,
Hidden under the ground.
Winter is not the season
Of the cheeky, red squirrel.

The cheerful song of the robin
Can be heard throughout the land.
And this boastful bird is seen
Showing off his scarlet vest.
The winter season belongs
To the bright, chirpy robin.

Nick Hinchcliffe (11)
Fullwood, Sheffield

The lavender field

The mauve colour of the field,
Makes me come and dance.
With the sunset behind
The green, green trees glisten
As the wind whistles through the lavender.
As it is cut down
With a scythe, all of Norfolk smells.

Jenefer Leach (9)
St George's Middle School,
Dersingham, Norfolk

Clouds

I think
that clouds are
giant cats
purring across the sky.
Their tails fluffy
And their purring
is the wind.

Vincent Muddle (6)
Whitehills Lower
School,
Kingsthorpe,
Northampton
(Highly commended)

Gifts

Long ago in the sea
Coral grew and amber floated.
Pearls in shells formed from grit,
Like a speck in your eye.

Harish Sehdev (7)
Barton Hill J.M.I. School,
Bristol

Smells

Sweet is the smell of honey made by bees,
Musty the smell of the falling leaves,
Damp is the smelly, old and dark room,
Cold and wet is the smell of the tomb.
Putrid the smell that lingers on the farm,
Salty the smell of the sea, gentle and calm.
The aroma of flowers hanging on the breeze,
The nasty smell of pepper that makes you sneeze,
Spicy are the herbs that float around,
And sweet are the petals that tumble to the ground.
Some smells are sweet,
Some smells are sour,
Different are the smells that pass by each hour.

Bryony Howard (11)
Kitbridge Middle School,
Newport, Isle of Wight

November

And so, once more, the wood seems dead.
Scattered with relics of its summer beauty.
And the trees are grey like pillars,
Standing in the stone hall of time.

Alyson McGaw (13)
Wirral County Grammer School for Girls,
Wirral, Merseyside

Sweet Dream

Pushing the sun along in my pushchair,
She giggled,
So did I,
And woke myself up.

Adele Inugai-Dixon (4)
Stoke Park, Ipswich
(Highly commended)

Reindeer report

Chimneys: Colder
Flightpaths: Busier
Driver: Christmas Father that is
Still baffled by postcards.

Children: More
And stay up later
Presents: Heavier
Pay: Frozen

Mission in spite of all this
Accomplished.

Daniel South (13)
Wymondham High School,
Wymondham, Norfolk

Rainy days

Rain is thin
It is a ball of water
It lives up in the sky
When it rains it tickles
My knees
And makes me all wet.

William Beckerson (6)
Shottermill County
First School,
Haslemere, Surrey

Winter Beauties', Lucy Barnard (10)
(Highly commended)

My hyacinth poem

Hyacinth hyacinth how do you grow?
I grow by water
I do not eat anything
I love to be the colour of me
In me I have yellow bits
The only thing I do not like is worms
And slugs.
When I do not get water I die
And that's the end of me.
My smell is beautiful
It is just like perfume.

Loukia Avvakoumides (6)
Shottermill County First School,
Haslemere, Surrey

Moon

The moon,
A cultured pearl,
Hanging motionless over the ivory-blue river,
Sadly crying silver tears.

The ripples waver on the shore,
And the moon begins to dance limply over them,
The trees' tips reach up for the dusty sky,
Casting their threatening shadows.

The night lets out a faint whisper,
As the trees creak like a stiff door,
The solid silence hangs again in the wilting air.

A fish with its pearl-barley scales,
Leaps out of the creamy-white water,
Displaying its marble eye,
As it shimmers jade in the light.

Lucille Pearson (11)
Kingston upon Thames, Surrey

The wind

There is a wind wolf coming down the street.
It blows down trees as it goes along.
'Look out!' people say as they walk down the
    street.
It goes down the street to find a different house to
    rattle.
It ruffles your hair.
It snatches your breath away.

Andrew Simpson (7)
St George's V.C. Junior School,
Wembdon, Bridgewater,
Somerset

Fog

Fog is mist and
I can't see when
I am in it.
It's cold and wet.
It's like being in a parcel.
One that moves.

Jonathan Rushbrook (6)
St Thomas of Canterbury
Infant School,
Brentwood, Essex

Conkers

When chestnuts are hanging,
above the school yards
they are little green sea-mines,
spiky and hard.
But when they fall,
they burst,
and all the boys race.
Each shines as a jewel
in a satin case.

Lynette Foot (10)
New Bradwell C.C. School,
New Bradwell, Milton Keynes

Green

Walking home
Caught in a green mist
Feels magic
Up up high the mist takes me
Land in a green land
Emerald pale dull green
Mist coming down again
Green shape appears
Long green shape sliding slimy
Mist going slowly away
The shape is a snake
Green as green can be
Emerald pale leaves
Twinkling bright leaves fall on to the snake
Fall on to his glittering scales
The snake turns emerald
Toads croak
Croaking toads croak croak croak
The mist comes back turning emerald pale dull
green
Jumping into the mist I go
The snake goes hiss hiss
Toads croak in the magic mist
Sailing up into the sky
Drops me down
I hope I never see green again

Joanne Birch (7)
Marston Green Infant School,
Marston Green, Birmingham

My Christmas thought

Robin Redbreast
On a silver tree,
Glowing in the moonlight.

Cherry Hiscox (6)
Gaer Infant School,
Newport, Gwent

The midwinter goddess

She walked, tall and dazzling,
As a flame,
Chilling,
Blue in her fury.
The cold, hard ruler;
Goddess of seasons.
She was clothed
In ice of blue and white,
And slept in a bed of
Interwoven frost.
She marched past Autumn,
Who bowed down,
Sending down showers
Of golden brown leaves,
As tokens of respect.

If Spring is the mother of life,
Then Winter is the Queen of Death.

Thomas Bazeley (13)
Bradford-on-Avon, Wilts

122

Winter patterns

The cardboard cut-out trees,
Stark and flat
Against a paper sky,
Painted with watercolour clouds.

This sky sends
Colour-coded weather forecasts
To the old men that sit upon the bench;
Now it is pale grey,
Like cigarette smoke
Coughed out from an old man's lungs.

A mole's skeleton lies,
Just a geometric heap
Of bleached matchsticks,
Blood run into the quartz snow.
I crush it with my boot.

I look behind me
And see the snow
Doodled with trees, shrubs
And footprints,
Like a doubtful page
Of a writer's mind.

Jude Fitzgerald (13)
Halesworth Middle School,
Halesworth, Suffolk

The Conch

The conch is a beautiful shell,
So smooth inside,
Where the snail lived,
A Chinese temple, with spiral staircase.
A pearly, pinky, colour.
It's very hard,
And the brown scale
Starts flaking to white.
In fairy tales
Mermaids use them for horns,
To blow,
It seems as if the conch
Lived in a palace.

Victoria Booth (7)
St Cedd's School,
Chelmsford, Essex

Places and Objects

Reflections

The water is yellow and orange
from the reflections of the sun.
The swan admires herself in
the rippling waters,
Buildings cast long dark shadows
on the crystal lake.

Men walking on their heads look
strange as they kick their legs
in the air.
And the arched bridge looks
like an eye without a pupil.
The clouds sail under the chimneys,
and two cats walking past
look as if they are walking
on their backs.

Elen Williams (10)
Y Bontfaen Primary School,
Cowbridge, S. Glam

My bike

My bike is muddy
Mud splashes on my back
When I ride
My saddle is soft
My pedals sparkle in the sun.

Simon Gicquel (7)
Lodge Hill Infants School,
Caerleon, Gwent

The photo

A photo is a thread in time
waiting to be pulled.
The memories that come alive,
untied from the spool.

Theresa Balcombe (12)
Rye, E. Susse>

The land nearest the sky

India.
The land nearest the sky, so I'm told.
A moving rainbow.
A million people clad in multicoloured silks.
The rejahs carrying pots of clay,
Their silver, gold and ivory jewellery
Jingling as they toil.
The rickshaw driver.
His feet scattering the ochre dust
As he carries his passengers
Through the streets.
Into the bazaars,
Where mountains of green and red chillis,
Garlands of flowers and baskets of exotic fruit,
Colour the scene and scent the air.
The temple, cool and tranquil.
The dancers.
Their dark, liquid eyes stare
As they move with the grace of Siva,
In time to the haunting sound of the drum.
A hazy sky filled with the pale smoke
From countless sticks of burning incense.
This is India.
The land nearest the sky.

° rejahs — *working women*
  Siva — goddess of grace and peace

Kate Davies (15)
Failsworth School,
Failsworth, Oldham

The street where I live

I walked down the street and what did I see?
Lots of windows looking at me,
A pillar box shiny red,
A shop that sells cakes and bread.

The betting shop painted green,
With horses as lean as a runner bean.
Trees, trees, that make me sneeze,
Green leaves rustling in the breeze.

People rushing to and fro,
Where are they going?
I don't know.

There's the surgery, long and low,
That's the place where most of us go.
Mumps and measles, all those things,
Sometimes a needle and my arm stings.

Group Work (4/5)
Barton Hill J.M.I. School,
Bristol

The plughole

Did you ever hear a plug being pulled out?
Pop! The monster squeals
Then it begins sucking water
Down into its deep dark depths
Gurgling and gulping.
One last swish and a burp
The whirlpool fades
And the pipes start to groan.

Lisa Sutherland (10)
Linlithgow, W. Lothian

'The Safari Park', Kirsteen Ann Harvey (4)

129

At Dunwich

At Dunwich
You can wander through the forest,
The ground sprinkled with pine needles,
Littered
As the floor of a bird's nest,
The moth-wing prints
Of rabbits' paws
Winding through bushes,
The pine trees
Spearing the sky,
Giant quills
Sucked dry by blotting paper clouds.
Ivy,
Knotting through a barbed wire fence
That has rubbed off rust
On to the blistering stems.

At Dunwich
You can shuffle through sand
On the oil clotted beach,
Swelling your head
With the salty smell
Of fresh cod.
Seagulls
Gliding on air currents
As they fly in the wake
Of the fishermen's trawlers.

At Dunwich
You can walk the cliff tops.
Grass,
Bristle cut in tufts
Sprouting out from behind mole hills.
Skeleton trunks
Of dead trees
Lining the path,
As the edge creeps gradually nearer,
Falling prey to the sea.

At Dunwich
You can stand,
Looking at the last gravestone
Eaten by lichen,
Branded by the irons of decay.
A subtle mound
Of darker grass,
Waiting,
Waiting to melt over the cliff
And join other graves,
Lost at sea . . .

At Dunwich.

Lara Mair (12)
Halesworth Middle School,
Halesworth, Suffolk
(Arthur Lines Poetry Award winner)

The Liner

The whale blows its funnel,
A grey wall ploughing through the waves
Its propellor churning,
The sun glinting on its metal skin.

The ship pulls out of the docks,
Pushing its muscly body,
Puffing its blow hole,
Smashing the waves with its powerful tail.

Katherine Currie (13)
Billericay School,
Billericay, Essex

Owed to a fruit machine

One more coin
won't hurt
One more coin
could be the difference
between starvation and tomorrow
One more coin
and nothing else
for today.

Through the slot
of a metal machine
Through the slot
and into oblivion
deciding whether I win or lose
Through the slot
and nothing else
for today.

Turning reels
that spin
Turning reels
that have the power
to answer all my prayers tonight
Turning reels
and nothing else
for today.

Lemon, cherry, bar
no win
Lemon, cherry, bar
has destroyed my dreams
but rekindled the craving
Lemon, cherry, bar
and nothing else
for today.

One more coin
won't hurt
One more coin . . .

And nothing else . . .

Catherine Wilkinson (13)
Buckden, Huntingdon, Cambs

Special Phrases to Encourage Lazy Limousines

Rev the engine, change the gear,
Fumes expel from the rear.
Everything is far from well,
I think it's time to use a spell.
Anti-freeze and motor oil,
WD-40 on the coil.
Monkey wrench and battery charger,
Turn this wreck into a starter.
If my words you haven't heeded,
Stronger terms are sometimes needed.
Esso! Mobil! Texaco!
Should make your engine Go, Go, Go.
Sing the virtues of Amoco,
Speak the incantations low.
Sparking plugs, contact points,
Dynamos and seized ball-joints.
Alas, some don't respond to magic,
And their final fate is tragic.
Curse and damn them for being phoney,
Send their remains to the evil Taroni. *

° Taroni is a scrap yard in Birmingham

Rebecca Bayliss (12)
Great Barr School,
Great Barr, Birmingham

Crabbing on the mud-flats

We push the boat a little way out,
And climb in.
We are after the shellfish tanks,
That haunt the murky waters.
I uncoil my line,
And tie on my bait,
A slimy, gory,
Fish-head.
Hard with bone,
Yet limp with death.
My line is already dampening,
Clogging up with grease.
Its weights pull it to the bottom
Like water-filled wellies on tired feet.
I pull it up,
Heavier than before.
Three small crabs,
Like tiny flattened flower-pots.
With four roots sticking out each side,
And two thin bulbs at the front.
They grip the line like limpets.
I pull them into the boat
And drop them into the temporary tub.
We fill it up,
Then Chris says:
'Let's use me wellies!'
We have a boot each,
And then recast our lines.
I drag mine up,
Bigger, more plentiful,
Better than before:
'This one must be the best yet!'

My bait is deep in crabs
As was the Garden of Eden with fruit.
Some miss the narrow neck of the boot
To drop on the seat,
Like hailstones on an old tin roof.
I go to pick one up,
And it grabs me.
Hanging on with caliper-like pincers.
The pain is sharp and sudden,
Like the popping of a balloon.
But it drones on
A long crescendo
Hurting more each minute.
Shouting and swearing,
I try to shake it off.
It slackens bit by bit
Like a loosening screw,
Finally to drop,
With flailing legs,
On the bottom of the boat.
'I'll do 'im!'
Chris picks up some weights,
Hefts them in his hand
Like a cricketer,
But throws them like darts.
The crab lies smashed
A splintered shell.
Mangled,
Like a thrown away scrap of tin foil.
Soon the boots are almost filled
And the screaming sun beats down on two aching
    necks.
Two younger kids come over
And pester us like midges.

136

'Ooooh!!'
At the crabs,
'I wanna go! I wanna go! Pleeeease?!'
At me.
I shrug and hand one my line.
My hand seems to creak,
As I open and close it.
Slowly, cautiously,
I feel as if there's something;
Something I'm afraid of.
I turn to climb out of the boat.
My underused legs
Clamber clumsily to catch up with my arms.
I heave myself over the gunwale
Searching for the bottom with my feet.
But I push too far:
Over the top,
I fall in . . .
And the paint-cracked boat mocks me.

Stephen Gardam (12)
Halesworth Middle School,
Halesworth, Suffolk

Cross Street

One afternoon I walked to Cross Street.
I saw houses and buildings.
There were doors that were black and white
Leading into dark passages.
Kitchens warm with fresh baking.
Shops that smelt of oatmeal dog biscuits.
People hurrying,
Or looking in shop windows,
The wind blowing their scarves.

Kelly-Marie Keen (6)
The Beacon Infant School,
Camborne, Cornwall

Bath tub by candle light
(from Bonnard's 'The Bath Tub')

Green water, blue, chalk-white
she lies in this elongated marble
of light and shape and clarity.

Tiles coat her legs
she is pane-thin, supine,
cut from paper.

A fly melts into the paisley lime
that licks her skin
and chokes when she moves.

Absolute here,
she is this light
this vanilla-sweet warmth.

If you reached for the line of
filament black, around her skin
you could not hold it.

See. The face smiles
'You cannot touch me.
I am detached.'

Melting wax cuffs the chain
of mercury beads
as a curled toe lifts.

This liquid volume of iris-flint
glass, is pulled away
from the shape she has made.

Alice Allen (16)
St Lawrence, Jersey,
Channel Islands

Candle

The flame
Is a key off an ash tree,
That flickers
In a draught.

The wax collects
Like water ladled in a leaf.
Then spills,
And rolls down.

Wax, hard and cold,
Hanging from the holder.
A baby's saliva
Waiting to drop.

Shadows, an insect,
Trapped at a window.
Frustrated movements,
Captured by the candle.

The wick, now blown.
A soot-stained cobweb.
And smoke, thick, twirling
Like ink in water.

Thea Smiley (12)
Halesworth Middle School,
Halesworth, Suffolk

Warmth in the rain

In the travel agent's window
the advert stares blindly
at the bank across the road.
Black volcanic sands of Tenerife
with azure waters behind.
Sun drenched palm trees are
like pineapples with no flesh.
The wave is about to break
on the acid pitted rocks.
The blazing sun has made the
temperature soar like a
shaken champagne bottle cork.
The youth, chewing gum
walks away into the grey drizzle
dreaming of the sun.

Heather Tewkesbury (13)
Stourport-on-Severn High School,
Stourport-on-Severn, Worcs
(Highly commended)

'Statue', Loretta Hayes (17)
(Italian Tour Award winner)

The barn

Down the old lane,
Where old puddles are now
Filled in with new gravel.
On past the house and the gate –

That's where the old barn lies,
Its once red roof now pink with age.
The old table, the tools and hay,
A child's play palace.

142

The old beams creaked and groaned,
As I swung to and fro on the rope swing.
Then up and up on the bales of hay,
Until finally, I was king of the castle.

It was a battlefield where wars were won,
An intergalactic space station,
A formula one racing track —
And occasionally even a barn.

Years have passed since then.
The wars are over now,
The space station is gone,
The race track closed down.

Now for me, the barn is just a barn.
Lying in wait for my successor.
Waiting again for a spirit
For imagination.

Declan McKeveney (14)
Lismore Comprehensive School,
Craigavon, N. Ireland

Motorway manoeuvres

Foot to the floor
Dad's at it again
Engine note rising
speeds, rev counter climbing
Blast through into the fast lane
kiss the lorry goodbye
Fat tyres hugging the road
A fine spray, producing a rainbow tail.
That car, it's coming up too fast,
get out of the way, move!
Brake, hard, tyres screaming
waiting for the inevitable crunch.
It never comes
Pretty close, eh?
Yes Dad, it was.

Neal Patel (14)
Cardiff High School,
Cardiff
(Highly commended)

Fantasy

The witch of Clignart

The witch of Clignart did no bad,
In fact, the Devil was the only thing that made her
    mad.
She's the daughter of God some people say,
But, more likely a spirit from the land of May.
She built the City of Clignart for the Dukes of
    Champagne
And raised the Pyrenees for a frontier against
    Spain.
Now she lives halfway up the Eiger
With Saladin the frog and Arian her pet tiger.

Andrew Martin (8)
Reevy Hill First School,
Buttershaw, Bradford

The unicorn

The unicorn screamed.
What was it that had startled it
While it ate pseudocarps from the trees?
Again it happened,
Lightning flashes from the
Roof of the heavens.
The sky was scarlet,
The moon on fire,
Howls of the wind were mingled with
Sounds of lightning
Striking for its prey, a noise like
Fingernails scraping on stone.
Waves of terror hit the unicorn
Frozen to the spot, it
Struggled mentally to free itself, but to
No avail.
The lightning ran down its horn,
Dissolving its body
Turning what was flesh into electricity.
Rippling waves of kilowatts became its
Mane, purple fire its tail.
The earth herself cried out for help, even
She could not hold this
Burning beast of fire.
The lightning burnt out the unicorn's brain
Electric madness taking its place,
The unicorn screamed.

Suzanna Fitzpatrick (11)
Newstead Wood School,
Orpington, Kent

The magic box

I will put in the box
The cry from a new born baby,
The growl from a hungry lion,
And the fear of its victim.
I will put in the box
The song of a bird,
A twinkle from the stars,
And the light from dawn.
I will put in the box
A grain of sand from a faraway beach,
The bark from a lonely dog,
The night and the day.
I will put in the box
The laughter and excitement of a child,
Yesterday and tomorrow,
And the sun and the moon.
My box is rain on the outside
And sunlight on the inside.
It has fire and snow mixed
Together as its lid,
Which I close and attach wings.
I fly it away to an edible island
With seas made of chocolate
And sand made of sugar.

Lauren Wilce (10)
Northmead County Middle School,
Guildford, Surrey

Split personality

She laughs and tries on another hat.
Red this time, with a few feathers.
'I'm the devil now,' she says,
And glances wickedly around.
Catching sight of me in the mirror,
She says 'Hello, I'm the devil!'
Her friends laugh and place another hat in her
    hands.

Now the hat is black.
Black for evil,
For sadness,
For absolute nothingness.
'I'm at a funeral,' says the girl,
And picks up another hat;
As the friends collapse weakly around her
Laughing and giggling.

'A blue hat for a blue day,'
She sings.
The other girls join in for a while.
The girl prances around.
As she tilts the hat forward,
They start to giggle again.

'A green hat, I think,'
And on it goes.
'No, I don't like this,
It's miles too big.
I look like a hunter
In the jungle,'
She says
'I'm going to stalk a giraffe!'

'Got it!' she says,
And pounces on a yellow hat.
It's too much for her friends
As they gasp, and hold their sides.
'You know who I am now?'
She asks.
'I'm Banana Man!'
One girl shrieks hysterically,
Staggers, and knocks hats everywhere.

A shop assistant hurries over
And gives a sharp reprimand.
The girls drift away, still laughing.
I put the yellow hat back reluctantly,
Sober now,
Myself once more.

As I leave the shop
I glance in the mirror.
The other girl sees me
And gives a quick wink.
I grin and walk out.

Karen Taylor (15)
Tarporley, Cheshire
(Highly commended)

The cyclops

Cave-dwelling
Year after year, the
Cynical cyclops
Lives by the shore.
One-eyed giant,
Polyphemus, the
Sailor-swallower!

Catherine Smart (11)
London

'Venice Carnival', Miranda Stacey (16)

The true story of Jack and the beanstalk

Now listen well and don't start yawning
For this my tale should be a warning.
'Tis about an awful boy called Jack
Who was a kleptomaniac.

His family lived in poverty,
A sorry way for them to be,
But 'twas these early childhood days
Which influenced his thieving ways.

One day, when things weren't going well,
His mother sent Jack out to sell
The family cow, which, she had hopes,
He might sell for some meagre groats.

But Jack was not a clever lad,
And met a con-merchant who had
Some magic beans, or so he told,
And them he soon to Jack had sold.

He was not far away from home
When Jack realized what he had done.
He thought, 'Why did I sell that cow?
My mum'll really kill me now.'

When he got back she spanked him sore,
And threw the beans out of the door,
She cuffed him twice around the head,
And sent him up the stairs to bed.

His sleep was not a peaceful one
As he dreamt of what he might have done
And when he woke at six o'clock
There stood outside a large beanstalk.

'Aha!' he thought, 'It does look high
And reaches right up through the sky,
Winding, winding all the time,
I think I'll go and have a climb.'

At length he'd nearly reached the top,
But once there was forced to stop
For in the distance there was coming
A giant, fee, fie, foe and fumming.

He trembled at this vicious cry,
And, seizing a golden egg nearby,
Shinned back down the stalk, feet-first,
Arriving just in time for breakfast.

His mother was so pleased with him
He vowed to go back up again,
And did just that, the very next day;
A stupid idea, some would say.

This time he reached the giant's lair
And found another gold egg there,
But just as he was looking round
He heard the giant's tell-tale sound
And, scampering right back down the tree,
Reached his home and warm safety.

By now young Jack was self-assured
And greedy thoughts of treasure lured
Him back up to the giant's house,
And in he crept, quiet as a mouse.

The giant sat snoring. Beside his legs
Sat the goose which laid the golden eggs.
Quick as a flash Jack snatched it round,
But all too late he now had found
That such a goose cannot be harmed —
It had been burglar-alarmed.

Of course, the giant caught poor Jack,
And ate him with a wholesome CRACK!
Which in a way just serves him right,
He really wasn't very bright.
But criminals aren't, are they now?
And crime don't pay, so keep your cow.

Evan Lees (14)
Hutchesons Grammar School,
Glasgow

New colour

I almost grasped it; then
  it slipped
      just beyond
        and beyond,
This primary
begotten of red-yellow-blue,
compound element
of three different hues
of identical white
And this desire
  too great
     much too great
to paint with it
or to achieve
one greatness
one triumph
alone.
But this colour
is triumph,
is greatness
alone,
So I paint rainbows
  because it slipped
     just beyond
       and beyond.

Clare Connors (15)
Debenham High School,
Stowmarket, Suffolk
(Highly commended)

A witch's cure for George

Some blood from a dragon
A wing from a fly
A stripe from a tiger
A dinosaur's eye
An egg from an eagle
A piece of the moon
Some fangs from a viper
And a hairy baboon;
A tail from a lion
And half of a skull
A vampire bat's wing
And a beak from a gull;
A leg of a spider
And half of a frog:
A shell from a snail
And some slime from the bog.
Put these in a cauldron
And mix for an hour,
Then leave it for a week
In a burglar-proof tower.
Then take it out
And put it in a cup
And if George eats it
He should stand up!

Martin Douch (10)
Tring, Herts

Monstrous night

As the wind howled, the branches beat against
The window pane, casting long deep shadows
Right across the room.
Little Sam sat shivering on his pillow
And listened to the rumbling, grunting
From beneath his bed.
Then to his horror there appeared
A tail, green, spiky, broad and crusty
Like a monster thorn.
This was closely followed by a pair
Of gigantic muscular legs; on each a russet orange
    foot
With lurid luminous claws.
A scaly back, with black and silver zigzag markings.
Steamy pebbled skin like warrior's mail,
Finally pulled clear.
Sam watched and saw a grizzly lizard head
With nostrils puffing pungent flames,
Lunge clumsily towards him.
A thousand pounds of flesh climbed on his bed,
Hideous scaly arms, tentacles quivering,
Lumbered closer.
The monster oiled its way up along the bed,
Its metallic eyes rolling and glinting in the
    moonlight,
Its jaws open in a grin
Exposing a fence of dagger-like teeth.
It raised its massive slimy body
High up above the petrified boy.
Its colossal reptilian chest crashed down
On Sam and crushed his bones to dust
And plunged him into darkness.

'Wake up Sam, you've overslept.
You'll miss the bus
And Mrs Hinton will be cross.'
Sam looked around,
The monster'd gone.
The room was filled
With golden sunlight.

Nicola Burgess (11)
The Lady Eleanor Holles School,
Hampton, Middx

Crazy Countries

Australia turned Hungary
While Great Britain
Put Greece into Japan
And topped it with Chile.
While this was going on,
New Zealand was turning old
And China was smashed.
It was Russia (rush hour)
In Argentina
Where someone, somewhere
Was eating Brazil nuts.
In the U.S.A. someone was saying,
'Alaska if she wants some Turkey.'

Duncan Robertson (11)
Dulwich College Prep School,
Coursehorn, Kent

A Christmas Tree's Dance

A Christmas tree twinkling,
In her ballroom dress,
When midnight comes,
She awakes,
As the hour strikes,
She yawns and stretches,
Her branches tingling with joy.
The tinsel sparkles,
The baubles jump,
The angels sing loud and clear,
As the tree polkas out of the house.

She looks up at the stars,
The calm clear night,
With the moon smiling down,
She twirls and waltzes,
Till she's dizzy,
But she still carries on,
Then the church bell strikes one.
All is over,
Slowly the Christmas tree climbs back
Into her pot,
And as all is quiet
She sleeps.

Marny Cliffe (11)
Christleton County High School,
Christleton, Chester

Opposite

If everything was opposite
Why, less would be more
The tramp would be rich
And the Queen would be poor.

Aeroplanes fly underground
Submarines swift in the air
Two would be single
One as a pair.

The bride at her wedding
Would look lovely in black
The crowd at the funeral
Would have white on its back.

The tortoise, fast
The hare, slow
The green light means stop
The red light means go.

If things were opposite
What turmoil there'd be
I would be you and
You would be me!

Susan Atherton (14)
Holy Cross R.C. High School,
Chorley, Lancs

Straight lines

As I lay in bed,
Gazing up at my mum,
Her earrings were swaying,
Hypnotizing,
Long and thin,
Swaying, slowly.
Suddenly
The earrings
Turned into swords
Swaying,
In battle, two men,
Fighting, lances clashing;
Then it was gone,
And a leopard jumped
Out of the lance,
Ladies screamed,
Loudly,
Penetrating noise,
It ran along, fast,
Challenging all it met!
Away, into the night.
Then, it vanished.
Into a room,
Lights flashing
Ladies dancing,
Dresses flowing,
Glasses clinking.
A piano,
Playing,
The keys bold and strong,
Fingers, drumming,
Black then white.

Black, then white,
Newspapers' pages
Turning,
Over and over,
A head,
Nodding,
Behind the paper,
Slowly,
Reading,
Word after word,
Page after page,
Black, then white,
Black and white,
The zebra's
Stripey back,
Straight and strong,
Hard and stiff.
Stripe after stripe,
Black, then white.
Black then white;
Driving along the motorway,
Straight and long,
Never ending.

Hannah Carter (13)
Newbury, Berks

The thing

It was a still night as the vibrantly blinding moon
   shone.
In the distance a howling was heard, screeching,
   deafening.
The moon seemed to move closer, closing me in
   my space.
The noise grew louder and louder till my ears were
   burning.
I walked faster, my footsteps pounding in my head
   at a constant heavy beat.
There was a cold shiver down my spine,
My heart beat at a rapid speed as my blood rushed
   around my body.
Close by I could hear footsteps I wasn't quite sure
   whether they were mine
or someone else's because my footsteps were still
   rumbling throughout my head.
Turning around, I saw something, something quite
   terrifying.
Bloodbound fingers is what I distinctly remember
   like red wine pouring out of a bottle.
In this mass were fingernails hardly recognizable
   because of all the blood.
The eyes of the creature, blue like sapphires,
   shone, hypnotic.
I looked away then back again, it was at this point I
   realized it was injured.
Its back covered with blood like a stream flowing.
The sticky thick blood clung to the thing's brown
   fur.
The eyes kept on staring at me waiting for me to
   look into them.

I knew if I looked into those paralysing eyes I would
    feel the suffering it was feeling,
Even so, I stared trying to fight the pain,
I looked away but some force brought me back.
I could now feel a constant sharp pain through my
    body,
I was starting to grow weaker like I was withering
    and dying.
The evil but beautiful eyes looked at me pleading
    for help.
I could not stand it anymore, I wanted to help but I
    wasn't strong enough,
I turned around and ran into the night.
Hearing the Thing's howling in the distance behind
    me.

Rachel Madgewick (15)
Sowerby Bridge, W. Yorks

'Clay Man', Victoria Morton (16)
(Italian Tour Award winner)

Giant hands

Giant hands
can squash a house
and flatten it
like a pancake
very flat.

Giant hands
can hold a tree
and snap it up
as if it was a twig
and throw the bits about.

Adam Walker (6)
St Johns
C.E. Primary School,
Dukinfield, Tameside

Life and Death

Fear

You cannot see me,
I am invisible,
You cannot hear me,
I make no sound.
You cannot taste me,
I have no flavour.
You cannot smell me,
I create no odour.
But you can feel me,
You can feel me in your mind,
Terrorizing your thoughts,
Making the rational parts of your brain insane.
Wherever you go I will haunt you,
Because I am fear.

Nicholas Gladden (12)
St Anne's C.E. Middle School,
Bewdley, Worcs

You can take my blood

Doctor you can take my blood out
Doctor doctor I said
Take my blood out.
You can have some
If you want it.
To put in someone else.

Edward Cooper (7)
St John's R.C. First School,
Norwich, Norfolk
(Highly commended)

Hourglass

Grey day . . .
The clock-hands are ripping the hours away.
She sits,
And waits
For someone to colour her in.
She stares
From her shoddy shoebox 'home',
Sees the city dying.
She'd read the writing on the wall.
Multi-coloured murals,
The truth they tried to wash away.
She sighs a little . . .

Grey world . . .
She seethes
She writhes
She loathes this town.
Buildings claw upwards,
Sleet spits down.
Crumbling concrete congestion . . .
Smash the spiky skyline,
Stain the soulless steel,
Splash a sanguine red
Across the city's ugly weal.
Stifle spluttering chimneys,
Shake the scaffolding skeletons.
She cries a little . . .

Grey lives . . .
Drudging in the sludge.
In each sordid snaking street,
Shuffling, shivering, stumbling,
Scuffed shoes upon their feet.
Splinter their glassy calm.
Monotonous mechanics.
Wrench the grinding cogs and whining wheels
apart.
She wants to stab, to scribble, sear,
To scream and screech and shout,
To scratch and scrape and scald and scorch,
But her sap is all squeezed out.
She dies a little . . .

Grey heart . . .
She looks
In the mirror.
Sees a face
She does not know.
Inscribed.
Solitary.
Swimming in a sea of grey
Drowning.
She grasps
At something to trick Time's eye.
Bright red lipstick.
Scarlet smear.
Incongruous.
Clownish.
In her hourglass
The last grains trickle out . . .
She reaches
For something to tear Time away.
The razor's steely sting against her wrists.
The clock strikes thirteen,
She turns her dying head,
A silent second splits,
And her grey grey world turns red . . .

Rosanna Lowe (15)
Kenilworth, Warwicks

Condemned

Condemned to do
What you do not want to do
Like a crisp brown leaf
Condemned to blow
Where the wind wants it to go.

Boris Wolff-Metternich (15)
Shiplake College,
Henley-on-Thames, Oxon

'Albion Alley', Robin Carrigan (16)
(Highly commended)

Motherhood in childhood

I can hear my mother's voice ringing plaintively
With cries to soften my deepest doubts
Of what it's all about.

'We're going shopping!'
'Get in the car!'

My stubbornness prevailed.

'Your mother says so, that's a good enough
    reason,'
Came a mature, male voice,
Which called itself my father.

Parents, with their lumbering bodies,
Try to squeeze through a sieve
Into a pudding bowl of dumpy childhood,
But their flesh is only cut on the wire strands.

My friends and I, we fled
Through the holes, daily,
Daily flights to the childhood den,
Where baby mushroom men
Ruled on sugar thrones.

Parents and time ate up the sugar.
We learnt to speak proper,
Stand straight, our heads up high,

'Till we sag again, faces drooping,
And death knocks upon the door.
I still remember the ambulance welcoming death
With its childish tooting siren.

Richard Gipps (13)
The King's School,
Canterbury, Kent

She's not really dead

It really is a nice coffin.
The flowers make it look nice.
It reminds me of Kate.
She is nice, was nice.
She's in there.
It's hard to believe
But it's her.
What's left of her.
Just a body really.
It's strange to think that I saw her
Just a few days ago.
Seems like years.
Seven years.
She was seven years old,
Almost a baby still.

I hate cars.
I won't ever drive again.
Nor will the driver,
The driver of the car.
Kate was hit by the car.
The car with the driver.
He shouldn't get drunk.
Pavements are different
— From roads.

'Ashes to ashes . . .'
Just like the explosion really
That hurt my eyes.
My eyes are hurting now.
Just itching.
I can't help rubbing them.
I wish I could rub the lump in my throat
It hurts.

I feel like crying.
I think I am crying
Or is it rain?

Why is this man shaking my hand?
He's got a funny collar.
Oh, of course, he's a vicar.
How silly of me!
Am I supposed to go this way?
No, I won't.
I haven't said goodbye
I can't go.
I can't leave her.
She'll be alone.
She's my sister,
I must stay with her.

Where is she?
At school.
Yes,
I've got to go and get her
From school.
She may get run over otherwise.
Busy road really.
Have to get a lollipop lady in orange and black.
The flowers were orange.
I'm in black.
Ah. Here's mum.
Come on mum, we've got to pick Kate up.
'Bye, vicar!
Look after the flowers.'

Karen Taylor (15)
Tarporley, Cheshire

Death

With blackness unrivalled he stalks,
He cannot be seen but is feared by all,

Over the old, suicidal and starving,
He casts his shadowy coldness,

His pain is shared by all in war, in peace,
Like a cold, cold bullet of steel,

His rain is a bloody red,
And his river is a murky pool of sorrow,

His coming is like the sweat,
Upon the fevered man's face,

The image of the dying baby,
The tears of the anguished mother,

His supper is the overdose,
Of the desperate addict's needle,

He smiles upon the murderer,
Who fills his bottomless pit of the dead,

He is there but cannot be touched,
He is death.

Darin Williams (13)
Meole Brace School.
Shrewsbury, Salop

Birth and death

The night Libya was doomed
The ginger cat
Queen of all cats
Gave birth
Her cries of agony and
The cries of Libya
Both met
In the middle of my mind
The cat's cry was stronger
It echoed around the house
From the TV I heard other cries
I switched off.
The screen was black.
I was silent.
After a few months
The heart of the ginger cat
Queen of all cats
Stopped.
Her death brought her kittens to me
But it was all over
For those Libyans,
And the ginger cat.

Franklin Puddefoot (10)
Weston Turville C.E.
Combined School,
Weston Turville, Bucks
(Highly commended)

Undercover of the night

Solo girl in a vile man's world,
Apathetic he took your life,
No sympathy, just a six inch knife,
And the darkness was his cover.

Fragile girl in a vile man's world
Like the dusk he crept behind you,
Enshrouded you, then murdered you.
And the darkness was his cover.

Defenceless girl in a vile man's world
Why are you not safe at night?
Drunk with violence, he abused your right.
You're just another . . . statistic.

Helen McLaughlin (14)
Holy Cross R.C. High School,
Chorley, Lancs

Gifts for Luke

You were longed for, Luke,
But when the time came on a cold, grey morning,
In a side room with a single bulb,
You were given to us too early
And later,
Taken too soon.

We fought with you,
Your tiny fists beating feebly against glass
(A fist as tiny as a man's thumbnail)
Small feet kicking at the air
(Feet which were never meant to walk, air
You were never meant to feel).

Five precious months
We were honoured to know you.
We loved and cherished you
Then one day,
Like a snowflake on a hot chimney,
You were

       gone.

Anne Diver (16)
Billericay School,
Billericay, Essex

It would have been alright

It would have been alright,
If Barry hadn't have been driving,
But he had.

It would have been alright,
If we'd seen the little boy,
But we didn't.

It would have been alright,
If we hadn't gone on the old deserted lane,
But we had.

It would have been alright,
If we hadn't found out that he was dead,
But we did.

It would have been alright,
If we hadn't been allowed the car.
But we had.

It would have been alright,
If Helen hadn't screamed,
But she had.

It would have been alright,
It if had been daylight,
But it wasn't.

Hannah Claughton (13)
Prince Henry's Grammar School,
Otley, Leeds

Death

He stands
In dark shadows,
In silent hospital wards,
In misty graveyards at midnight
Robed in black cloth,
A cloak and hood covering his skeletal form.
Carrying his scythe,
its blade of cold steel
dripping warm blood.
He glides silently
His face a grinning skull
a few flaps of putrid skin remaining,
kept on with black caked blood,
like a Hallowe'en mask.
His mind warped and black,
its depths of horror
filled with memories of lives taken
A murderer never brought to trial.

Barry Roberts (13)
Argoed High School,
Mold, Clwyd

Loneliness

Ships lie,
Some new,
Some old,
Some rusty,
Some shiny.
They wait,
They watch.
Waiting for fun
For life,
For excitement.
Seagulls glide and swoop,
Over the body of the ship,
Screeching a haunting cry,
Like a graveyard.
Mist descends.
Waters,
Calm, silent, unmoving.
A bright
Yet old orange ship,
Hums a one note tune.
Suddenly. . .
A pleasure boat chugs down,
Shattering the silence.
It jeers at the ships
As it disappears around the bend.
A triangle of waves
Circling out,
Spreading out
Lapping against the ships,
Awakening them from dreams and images.
Jolting their memories,
Wakening them to the fact.

Where they are.
Why they're there.
They lie forlornly
Staring,
Gazing
Up at the misty murky sky.
Put there by man;
Left to rust;
Left to rot.
It doesn't matter to man.
Man doesn't care.
Man won't hurt.
Man won't die.
The trees weep for them,
Large brown tears.
The ships heave a sigh;
They settle down,
Some to rust,
Some just waiting to go out to sea again.
Their home.
Small birds look solemnly on
With a wise knowing look.

Elizabeth Child (11)
Kea C.P. School,
St Kea, Truro, Cornwall

In loving memory

The idea was a challenge, we knew that.
We had no choice.
I thought he would listen but
I should have known better.
Pointless advice. Disregarded intentions.

We soared carefree until it happened.
I begged him but his conceit controlled him.

The sun penetrated the frayed feathers
Until it found the warm wax.
The plastic smell was overpowering.
First, his skin blistered,
Then the wings dropped as
Spheres of fire from Heaven.
His gliding ceased:
He dived towards his destiny.
The glistening waters seemed bleak.
Half dead already, he plummeted
Into the mouth of the sea;
The jaws of death.

Being clever killed him.

The water, once motionless, now rippled
As the carcase of his conceit
Floated to the surface.

We couldn't celebrate our victorious escape.
It was not victorious.

I hovered in anger and sorrow as
I waited to see his soul
Rise or fall.

Rachel Harvey (14)
Monmouth Comprehensive School,
Monmouth, Gwent
(Highly commended)

Nursery rhyme for war

Sing a song of massacre
the dead lie all around.

Four and twenty thousand
buried in the ground.

When the shells fly over
men drop down like flies.

Let's not forget the Glory
they're fighting for our lives.

Jennifer Evans (16)
Edenham High School,
Shirley, Surrey

The making of a new day

The slow air flowing through the body.
Now the darkness of sleep.
The squeaking of the wheeled bed.
The knife sliding across the body like an ice skater
on ice.
The bleeding river dammed by a cotton wall.
The new heart on an icy tray.
The sewing of the body like a new jumper being
made.
Life is born again.

David Hodges (11)
Crosshall Junior School,
St Neots, Cambs

The chess game

In the beginning all seemed equal
Then white made the first bold step.
Soon the black monarchy floundered
And seemed way out of its depths.

As bishops were crushed by a white ruler's path,
The black church began to disband;
All of its pawns had been captured
In a well-executed plan.

As the white front moved across the board,
The black queen seemed destined to die;
And the rooks which had once stood tall and still
Were now castles in the sky.

Any chance of a change was hopeless now,
As white took control of the game.
Black horses were starving in a barren land,
As they retreated, stumbling, lame.

White made a final, victorious move
And the black king fell and died
Then, there flourished white success;
And around it . . . apartheid.

Sarah Baxter (14)
The Mountbatten School,
Romsey, Hants
(Highly commended)

Behind closed doors

She kneels next to her bed,
Head bowed, hands clasped,
'God bless mummy and daddy.'
Mum tucks her up, safe and warm,
Kisses her head,
Admires her baby.
Dad looks in her room.
'Oh no God, please not again,'
He closes the door behind him.
She knows the routine,
Knows what Daddy expects,
Her little head filled with fear.
She screams,
Without making a noise,
Suffers in silence.
Afraid to look in his eyes,
The tears trickle down her soft skin,
She's so young, innocent,
A flower starting to bloom.
When he's satisfied,
He tucks her back up.
'Safe' and warm.
She listens to the bribes,
The promises,
Of course she won't tell,
She loves Daddy,
Daddy loves her.
He leaves her,
Closing the door behind him;
She prays again;
'Please God, I promise
I won't be bad ever again,
just stop him.'

Still she will pray,
night after night,
Everywhere little children
Screaming in silence.
But we're afraid,
Scared to look and pry,
Behind closed doors.

Jacqueline Robertson (15)
Sanquhar Academy,
Sanquhar, Dumfriesshire

In hospital

Doctors hurrying,
Nurses scurrying
And me worried in my room.

Doctors talking,
Nurses walking
And me listening in my room.

Doctors looking,
Nurses watching
And me lying in my room.

Doctors standing,
Nurses waving
And me going to my home.

Edward Mooney (7)
St John's R.C. First School,
Norwich, Norfolk
(Highly commended)

Learning and Work

In the exam room

Concentrate.
The papers twist over
With the rustle of fish tails.
Seaweed heads bend
Under anxiety,
Sweeping in tides
Between the rows.
My pen gleams,
Diffusing salty light.
The nib lies wet and ready:
But each line blurs and distorts
Into distant voices
I am sinking, slipping
Sliding from the pages,
The white wall of paper
Stands between death and sunlight
Floundering without air
I must write or drown.

Emma Crates (17)
West Wellow, Hants

Round here

They call this place a school, I think
I don't know I'd agree.
There are walls which tower high above us
Tiny glass windows with bars on them.
They say the bars protect the glass
From tennis balls. But ball games
aren't allowed round here.
So what's the point?
Broken points dug between the grooves
of desks. The ageing wood grain
battered, splintered, graffiti scrawled.
Desks uncared for. Graffiti
is not allowed round here.
But no one ever gets caught
in the act. Because no one ever
writes on desks. They say
it was here before.
Hours before
Hours in this place I give no name
Hours at home doing work
that they give you. Rules
that they give you.
And they straighten
And we bend
And they snap.

Catherine Wilkinson (13)
Buckden, Huntingdon, Cambs
(Highly commended)

Maths

I've tried counting in my head singing tables in my
    bed
Multiplying till I'm red that I'm most sure
Maths doesn't like me anymore.

Subtract and take away and minus in one day there
    isn't time to play and I'm quite sure
Maths doesn't like me anymore.

Number lines and magic squares all that jumping
    here and there
Doesn't get me anywhere
So I'm positively sure
Maths doesn't like me any more.

But for drawing I've a flair so I really shouldn't care
    but painting numbers that's not fair now I'm
    absolutely sure
Maths doesn't like me anymore.

David Woodrow (9)
Market Bosworth C.E. Primary School,
Market Bosworth, Warwicks

War poets

Most poets write
In studies;
Heated studies
With pens
Of the fountain sort.

But not the war poets;
They did not have
Studies to work in.
They wrote in the mud,
The slime, the dirt
of the trenches.
They wrote
While shells screamed
Round about them
And flew, whining
Into the sucking mud.
Among the soldiers,
The dead soldiers
Yet they wrote.
They gave the people
The news they needed.
The news the papers wouldn't print
In a searing way.

Matthew Cottingham (12)
Moulsford Preparatory School,
Moulsford-on-Thames, Oxon

'Downpour', Jennifer Kirk (16)

A poem entitled rain

'A poem,' she called at the top of her voice,
'Write a poem, for homework,' said she.
'That's easy for her to say,' said I,
'But it won't be easy for me.'

So I sit at the table, but feel quite unable
To think of a poem for she.
I think of the time, the rhythm and rhyme,
No, it isn't so easy for me.

I think of the rain, but it all is in vain,
Can't think of a poem for she.
'It was easy for her to say,' say I,
'But it wasn't so easy for me!'

Briony Chappell (13)
Alton Convent,
Alton, Hants

Writing a poem

Tension is building up on my pen
The syllables no longer seem to go
through my head
But straight to my hand,
for my hand is my mind now,

The words flood down to my paper,
    Trickling between the lines,
Up to the margin,
And beyond . . .

Shenna Bacon (12)
Sidcot School,
Winscombe, Bristol

Thoughts of a beginner

Walking sideways,
I'm doing it wrong,
But I find it hard with my feet so long.
I hope I don't do anything
I'll regret –
Thump! Ow! Up I get.

Must concentrate, mustn't talk,
I'm as steady as a baby
Learning to walk.
Don't stop now,
Let legs take strain.
Thump! Ow! Up again.

Third time lucky,
It can't be that hard.
Just take it gently, yard by yard.
Now get ready,
One . . . two . . . three . . .
Thump! Ow! Skiing's not for me.

Madeleine Bell (13)
Alton Convent,
Alton, Hants

Library blues

I'm here in the library
All is quiet,
Quiet as the night.

I'm surrounded by books,
I don't want to read,
But I don't put up a fight.
I could scream
And clear the shelves
Of the books and their coloured sleeves,
But I don't,
I sit and contain myself
As I look
From shelf to shelf
And book to book,
There's nothing
That makes me stop and look.
Aah! What's this?
It's big and fat,
I think it's about the law,
It would make a nice loud bang
If I dropped it on the floor!
I lean over and pick it up,
I hold my breath . . .
And then . . .
I sigh,
Put it back.
I should know better at this age,
But then again . . .
No, they'd know it's me,
I'd lose my job
Because
I work in this damn library.

Emma McCulloch (13)
Ewell High School,
West Ewell, Surrey
(Highly commended)

A lone boy is a sea of chattering heads,
All turned away from me.
It felt bad.
Then like 'Poseidon' calming a storm
The head master raised his hand,
And faces turned towards him in silence.
His monotone voice read out the exam results.
The boys cheered the scholars
And clapped those who passed.
But only 99 boys walked to the stage;
Only 99 boys were applauded;
Only 99 boys shook the headmaster's hand.
Only one did not,
One boy stood at the back of the hall
And the headmaster left the stage.
Never mentioning me
And the boys turned:
99 faces looked at me.

Andrew Hart (13)
The King's School,
Canterbury, Kent

Poet

The key to his work is
Discover his theme.
The theme of his work is
Repetition.
Repetition is the key.

Several of his ideas are stolen.
He seem to have no
Rhythm
But chops and
Changes his work to suit some
Inner purpose.

He never rhymes, except
When he does. Not inept,
Simply confused.

He has a strange view of things.
Distorted, warped, refracted
By a lack of sense of purpose.
There is a point,
A comment,
Somewhere,
But he cannot really express it.

To decipher him is easy.
Love is all you need.

Andrew Bedworth (16)
Aelfgar Centre,
Rugeley, Staffs

My poem

My poem wants the freedom of eternal length.
My poem is like an explosion of words in a deep
   imagination.
My poem refuses to spend the next twenty years of
   its life shut in a book gathering dust.
My poem longs to escape from its infinite maze of
   words.
My poem plummets from the purple skies to the
   centre of the earth like Cupid's arrow penetrating
   a frozen heart.
My poem lives for the world to hear and the sky to
   sing.
My poem waits for fire to freeze and ice to burn.
My poem has the gift of eternal youth.
My poem is against rubbers and correction fluids
   and word destruction.
My poem is for everyone unaware of its existence.

Catherine Wilkinson (13)
Buckden, Huntingdon, Cambs

Discipline

One times one is three.
Six times seven is forty two.
Battle of Hastings: 1066
         Answer!
Grey dawn outside.

Who was the first disciple?
Define a primary source.
Hydrogen, helium, lithium . . .
        Answer!
Cloudy morning outside.

A quadrilateral is a four-sided shape.
An adjectival phrase describes a noun.
Eight quavers in a four-four bar.
        Answer!
Rain slithers outside.

Je suis, tu es, il est . . .
Repetition intensifies descriptive passages.
Denote recessive genes: *b*.
        Answer!
Stormy afternoon outside.

One of the themes of the play is gemstones.
Use the subjunctive with *il faut*.
Dress carefully for interviews.
        Answer!
Shadowed twilight outside.

Have you done last week's accounts?
Where is the Brown file?
Don't forget to clock in.
        Answer!
Weekend. Paycheque.
Darkness falls outside.

Claire Milne (15)
Urmston, Manchester,
(Italian Tour Award winner)

Past, Present and Future

The battle of Hastings

We walked for days,
Marching, marching
Onwards.
Tired, exhausted,
Tasting defeat.
Messengers
Bringing bad news
William in England!

Up we get,
On the move,
Marching again,
Setting camp
Then marching,
Halt!
Nearly there.

Harold shouts 'Charge!'
Men advance,
Cavalry spots us.
What's that I hear?
Yells,
Screams,
Thundering of hooves,
Arrows flying,
Sounds of crying,
Shouts from men.
Clang!
Clash!
Swish!
Groans,
Pushing,
Shoving,
Banging.
Metal clinking,
Men dying.
Normans charging,
Horses falling,
Chain mail clashing,
Axes wielding.
Horses neighing wildly.
Men screaming,
Arrows killing men,
Arrows high
Coming down madly.
Harold's hit in the eye.
England is lost.
William is King!

Joel Busher (7)
St Chad's C.E.
Primary School,
Leeds

My home Culmailie

I gaze up at the two high mountains,
Ben Lundie and Ben Braghie.
They're like a king and queen
Sitting on their thrones
Watching over their kingdom.
The hills in the distance are their people,
The pine trees the bold soldiers guarding them.
The seagulls are like town criers
Screeching overhead.
The Lundie burn,
Like a snake, meanders down to the sea.
And the fields that surround them
Are the sovereigns' giant patchwork quilts.
The hens,
Like busy housewives
Chatter together
In high-pitched voices.
The horse,
With his head held high,
Like a sentry on duty
Guards the gates to his kingdom.

Rosalind Davies (10)
Struthers Primary School,
Muirhead, Troon,
Scotland

Terror at Lindisfarne

June 8th was the day,
The day when death struck
Lindisfarne.
I was hanging out the washing.
A cool breeze came off the sea
From the North.
I spied ships,
Great large long ships.

Bright sails
Birds of prey
Dragon heads.
I ran and told the other monks.
We went to greet them.
Horror met our eyes!
Great men manned the boats
Each with battle axes, swords or shields.
I hitched my habit above my knees
And ran!

Sally Seager (10)
Langton C.P. School,
Langton, N. Yorks

'The Battle of Maldon', Robert Kevin Howard (10)

Page three blues

Something amazing is happening in Basingstoke —
Ripped denim
Exposed flesh
A modern day Godiva
Rides around the town
On a one-two-five.
People gasp
Stare
Mothers hide their children.
Women, whose husbands read
The Sun in public
And *Playboy* in private
Comment on indecency.

Acceptable on public newsstands
Acceptable in print
In the flesh —
Outlawed.
The policemen who arrest her
Secretly admire
Her courage
Spunk
Frontal appendages.
Locker-room talk of
Page three models
Seems hypocritical
To the lone rider
Sitting
Waiting
Shivering
Imprisoned in a naked cell
Furnished only with a
Prickly cactus blanket of false virtues.

Catherine Burkinshaw (16)
Aylesbury, Bucks

The Natalon

The good ship *Natalon*,
Was sailing out on the tide,
Hordes of Spanish treasure,
Laden inside.

She had passed by way of Jamaica,
She had seen many foreign lands,
And now she was heading for Portsmouth town,
A fortune on her hands.

A stately galleon, luxurious and rich,
Colourful and gay,
A splendid diadem of England,
On that fateful day.

As the sun set off the Isthmus,
She left with crew and gold,
Bringing back from distant lands,
A fortune of splendour untold.

For laden in the hold that day,
Was a heap of golden treasure,
Ingots and gems, amethysts and jewels,
And rings too countless to measure.

Bearing amphorae and jars overladen with
    dubloons,
Sapphires and rubies glinting like the sun,
With bullion piled high in the amazing hoard,
The *Natalon* her fateful voyage begun.

The Captain was Sir Edward,
Of chivalry renowned,
A loyal man who would fight to the last,
Who would firmly stand his ground.

Faithful to land and King,
And to all he knew was right,
The Captain ordered his large ship on,
Plunging it into the night.

The steersman kept a steady course,
Plotting his direction east,
Though night and day passed away,
His labours never ceased.

Down below a lone guard,
Armed with musket and knife,
Forever guarded the treasure,
He protected with his life.

The crew were stretched on their hammocks,
Swigging flasks of rum,
Though all would soon perish,
Before the night was done.

On deck a few Marines stood,
Eyeing the pitch black night,
When all gasped, horror struck —
They could see an approaching light!

For, scything out of the mist,
A pirate vessel came —
The intruders fired a broadside,
Not to kill, but to maim.

On their minds was treasure,
Thus they prepared to board,
All their devilish thoughts,
Were set on taking the hoard.

The pirates threw over grappling hooks,
Which tore at the *Natalon's* stern,
At their head was a figure of dread,
The infamous Captain Kirn.

Yet another volley rang out,
Splintering the good ship's side,
Plucking up the sleepy crew,
And tossing them aside.

A brief exchange of shots,
And then they came aboard,
Brandishing guns and cutlasses,
Muskets and swords.

The Marines were hacked to pieces —
The same fate befell the crew,
The steersman lay dead, sprawled upon the deck,
But the attacking force grew.

Though the *Natalon's* men
Fought with valour great,
All of them that fateful night,
Would knock on death's black gate.

True, many pirates lay,
Bleeding on the floor.
But springing from their darting ship,
Rushed ever more and more.

Soon only the Captain and two marines
Were left alive on the deck,
And they alone could do very little,
Kirn's onslaught for to check.

Seeing all was lost,
Sir Edward took a powder casket,
Shooting this, not Captain Kirn,
With his last blast of the musket.

For none would keep the gold,
It would lie in the seas' domain,
As the ships erupted in a torrent of flame,
And every soul was slain.

So, to this day on the bed it rests,
Unseen to human eyes,
But what a tale it could have told,
Of its capture and demise.

Paul Groden (11)
Send, Surrey

Cooling down

Old woman stands,
Hands raised, pleading to a slowly setting sun.
Others hide, peering from behind closed curtains,
And a torn body lies, unclaimed, at the roadside.

Night casts its shroud over the battle ground.
I walk from the quiet city streets, out to the
    perimeter.

No one guards the barricades now,
Only the sick sweet smell of burnt rubber,
And a taste of ash in the still air.

I drag my feet,
Glass chinks,
Kicked along the tarmac.

A siren sounds,
Away in the distance a dog barks.
There's a static crackle of blue lights across the
    water,
And children run from the shop front
Into the side street shadows.

The moment passes;
Quiet again.

On the bridge,
Standing tall amongst the rubble,
I see a girl:
A wild flower in the moonlight,
Shining,
Calling out to us;
Calling out to them.

Oliver Shapley (15)
Beaminster School,
Beaminster, Dorset

Farewell Culmailie

You have been our home for generations,
Our shelter and our precious love,
Wisps of smoke now fill the air,
Burning embers smoulder there
Where once stood dear Culmailie.
The only trace of our forebears
Will linger in the rubble here.
We leave you now with heavy hearts
Our dear beloved Culmailie.

Louisa Winton, Mhairi Cruickshank (11)
Markethill Primary School,
Turriff, Aberdeenshire

I remember

'I remember,' she says,
'When I was a kid,
there were no worries,
we could go on the Ferry
to Liverpool and back,
or stay out till ten,
and my mum wouldn't worry,
down by the docks,
coming back from school,
we would talk to the sailors and fishermen.'

'As I remember it, this place that is,
wasn't an estate,
but all woods and fields,
we would come here for picnics,
and on Sundays, me, my mum, dad and Tom,
would all go to the beach,
we could leave the front door open, of course,
as I remember,' she says,
'but now you can't leave any door open,
or talk to people you don't know,
can't stay out till 8 o'clock,
even mum stays in,
dad doesn't like to be out either, after dark,
as I remember it,
we could stay out without going home, them days,
can't now.'

Mum says, 'Come straight home, love,
don't be late, you know how I worry.'
Those were the days, she says,
as I remember it,
she says,
as I remember it.

Rachel Girven (11)
Manor Junior School,
Birkenhead, Merseyside
(Highly commended)

'*Conway Mill Belfast*', *Ruth Mulvenna (17)*
(Italian Tour Award winner)

The end of Roman Britain
A lament by an Ancient Briton

The Roman road went on for ever
Like a story too old for you.
When did I think it would end? Well, never,
But it seemed they had other things to do.
The Picts, The Saxons, Goths and Huns,
They left us with them here,
We'd even learn to weigh in tons
If they'd stayed another year.
It seemed that they were going away
Soldier by soldier and slow,
Oh couldn't you stay another day?
I know you'll answer 'No'.
To think . . . at first . . . we fought them back!
It's hard to understand;
But of course, there's nothing on a hopeful track
With warriors raiding our land.
So now I've heard (my wife told me)
The Romans won't come home.
All those terrible invaders, you see,
Have sacked the stronghold — Rome!

Lucy Howard (8)
New Malden, Surrey

Sunday morning

Footfalls on time-tuned paving
Echo dustily
As the faithless faithful,
Fulfilling obligation,
Feign mute prayers
In coldstill air.

Music shiver-reaches gravestones
Borne on the bird song.

'Gothemessisended
Coffee will be served
In the porch.'
Congregations hunch home
Deaf, and beauty blind —
To each niche an icon.

Clare Connors (15)
Debenham High School,
Stowmarket, Suffolk

Motorway Mania

Dear Sir or Madam,

   We're glad to say
That the new M96 is coming your way.
In fact it's going smack through your flat.
I hope there's no offence to that
It's under the regulation act 74
If you don't come out, in come the law.
Of this reminder you will take note
Or you may swallow your antidote.
In your new flat these rules will apply
You can't smoke or drink, be nosey or pry.
You can't sit around or watch television all day
Mind you there's no aerial anyway.
One thing if you should wish to breathe,
Your flat you will have to leave
It's not allowed to smirk, smile or laugh
And certainly NO SINGING in the bath.

signed:

Michelle Carter (11)
Lostock Gralam Primary School,
Lostock Gralam, Cheshire

What am I?

I ripen the apples and melt all the snow,
I help all the trees and the plant-life to grow.
I put creases on faces,
And wrinkles in skin,
Help paper to peel and clothes to go thin,
I put holes in shoes which are worn day by day,
Change seed into grass and grass into hay,
I kill all the leaves on the trees and then,
I help them to grow all over again,
I open a bud,
Change egg into bird.
Change squiggle to letter and
Letter to word.
I change words on paper to story and rhyme;
Not who am I,
But what −
For you see,
I am time.

Melanie Uttley (15)
Rye Hills School,
Redcar, Cleveland

Pollution

Pollution doesn't swim, fly, run, jump, scuttle or
    scamper.
It glides along with its jet black gown.
In oil sewage and chemicals fishes drown.
On rusty metal and old tin cans,
Children cut their small soft hands.
In the fields and hedges small animals lurk.
Chemical spray will kill them, why not let nature do
    the work?
Litter all over villages and the town.
Pollution is coming in his jet black gown.

Pollution doesn't swim, fly, run, jump, scuttle or
    scamper.
It glides along with its jet black gown.
Acid rain killing forests and trees.
Rubbish blowing about in the breeze.
Nowhere for animals to sleep at night.
I hope the land will be all right.
It seems to me we live in danger.
Pollution is a horrible stranger.
Pollution is coming in his jet black gown.

Sarah Butcher (10)
Longborough C.E. Primary School,
Moreton-in-Marsh, Glos

The planet

Who would imagine that this swirling
ball of mist could be so full of wonders?
Every grain of sand is a galaxy in itself.
Animals that we think so tiny are suddenly
transformed into huge universes.

But turn it the other way round.
Our universe could just be another
grain of sand.

Katherine Fraser (10)
The Lady Eleanor Holles School,
Hampton, Middx

'Trawler leaving Grimsby', David Moorhouse (11)

Do not

Do not liken the emerald to the jade,
Do not dim the sunlight to the shade,
Do not see the truth as a charade,
Take what is and do not be afraid,
It is for you and yours the earth was made.

Claire Milne (15)
Urmston, Manchester
(Italian Tour Award winner)

The building site

Chomping robots,
Destructive machines,
Inquisitive schoolgirls
Peep over the fence.
Teachers lose their voices,
Assembly prayers are drowned,
Deafening thunderclaps
Seem to break your eardrums.
Monster destroyers.
'Danger!' screech the signs.
Orange metal dragons
Coated with wet mud.
Cumbersome creatures,
Could they lumber out?
Powerful, but clumsy,
They brickbash without mercy.

Huge monument erected
To the demolished bricks.
Turned to stone,
A statue scene.
White chalk bricks,
Steep mudbanks,
Slooshy slurpmud,
Chocolate, rich.
Precariously parked van,
Breezeblowing trees,
Traffic does not look twice
At the silent site.
How different it seems,
Now, in the silence time.

Lucy Howard (8)
New Malden, Surrey

Residences

Watching television
In your desirable
Detached house
What do you see?
A detached tent.
That must be desirable —
The place to be;
A thousand moved in yesterday.
With an *en suite* desert
And a good chance of a sun tan,
This unusual property
Is conveniently situated
For the next relief lorry.
Running water — occasionally —
Plus excellent opportunities
For catching dysentery.
Viewing by appointment
On world TV.

Danny Connors (14)
Debenham School,
Stowmarket, Suffolk
(Highly commended)

Before

What was here, before me? Before this printed leaf,
This tiresome assignment, this house – indeed
   what
Came and went, died and was born;
Worthwhile and forlorn,
Creatures existed and perhaps still do,
On the site, where this house –
Spiteful and greedy – denies the animals
Of their heritage and leaves them with none.

Perhaps a mouse did scamper in medieval sun,
Before the revolution had begun,
And his corn did hoard, in shaded den,
Before machines replaced the men.
Did knights in armour gallop by,
And damsels flounder, and tumble,
Escaping the Norse invasion's rumble?
Did Vikings on the horizon appear,
Carrying staff and sword and spear?

If they did, then they have gone,
There is just me and the poem-done.

Paul Coe (14)
Rawlett High School,
Tamworth, Staffs

For England

Everyone and everyone was
Bored.
Computers had taken over.
It was the people's fault —
They thought they were so clever
Programming computers
To do everything.
So
Everything was done
By computers.
The only jobs left
Were making and mending
Computers.
There were so many unemployed
That the government couldn't afford it.
The dole money was so low,
You couldn't even feed your pet on it,
Let alone your family.
Then . . .
A great idea.
Jobs for everyone.
No more boredom.
The people who had jobs
Would leave them.

And others would step in.
After a week, they would leave,
and the next lot start,
And so on and so on and . . .
So on. Every Sunday,
If you happened to be passing Dover way
At 2 o'clock precisely, you would see,
A large row of men and women,
Who had done their week's work,
Lined up along the White Cliffs
Brave Patriots,
Thinking they were doing a great thing,
'For England'.

(They are now known as the Red Cliffs of Dover)

Sue Warburton (13)
Stoke Park School
Coventry, W. Midlands

Striking Albert

Albert was a miner, he dug for lumps of coal,
Working out his days in a deep, dark hole.
He didn't find it pleasant, working down the pit,
But it did give him wages, so he couldn't really quit.

But then he joined a union, and soon got into
    trouble,
It told him to go on strike from sifting through the
    rubble.
He then started picketing, to try and stop the
    'scabs',
He didn't use violence, but up drew the police cabs.

The policemen had riot shields and truncheons
    they could use,
The pickets, they had nothing but lumps of brick
    and shoes.
Then a real war broke out, everyone joined the
    fight,
There were casualties on both sides, riots went on
    all night.

The policemen injured were put on stretchers, and
    quickly carried away,
The picket wounded lay on the ground and there
    they had to stay.
And on the news that night, it said how brave
    policemen were,
And listed the casualties and the charges they
    would prefer.

But it said nothing of the pickets, the first ones to
  fall,
No mention of Albert, the first casualty of all.
The bravery of the police was made much of for a
  year,
The bravery of the pickets didn't exist for all we
  hear.

Margaret Warman (12)
Newnham Middle School,
Bedford

How to enjoy life as a factory worker

Rules

1. Ignore the monotonous
    whirr of machines,
    the droning buzz
    of electric needles.
    Cut yourself off from the constant drawl
    of Radio One.

2. Preoccupy yourself in
    your own small world,
    accelerate down the straights
    and endure the most
    tricky detail — but make
    sure you enjoy it.

3.   Watch the way
      the fluorescent, clinical lights
      give the sheen to the
      one side of the material,
      and the way it drapes
      in folds for you when
      you have put more
      into it than any of the others.

4.   No smoking whilst creating please.

Thank you.

Chloe Downs (14)
St Edward School,
Charlton Kings, Glos
(Highly commended)

Surplus stock

Owing to advances
In medical science,
We now have a surplus
Supply of old people.
Yes, we are now
Almost giving them away.

New, especially for you:
A genuine granny,
Pre-packed in a plastic mac.
Next along the line, we've
A happy, yes happy, old lady,
Limited edition
So hurry up!
Call 0800-100-100
NOW!
We also have in our range
A lonely, uncared for old gent,
Now re-modelled, revamped
And re-packaged,
One grandad looking for
A good home.
To order any one
Of these old folk
Or to hear about the
Rest of our stock
Ring 0800-100-100
And quote your Visa or
Access Card number
NOW!

Danny Connors (14)
Debenham School,
Stowmarket, Suffolk

Revenge

YES! They now realize
She's human too.
Miss Lib, fed up with having her
intestines trampled by snap-happy tourists
Strikes with a flaming torch.
Oh yes, *real flames now*.

Zap, Zap, Zap, then
Splash, Splash, wading through
waist-high water which separates
Manhatten Island from
the ravishing Miss Lib, who,
usually placid,
beautiful crown, uncreased robes,
like an obedient housewife,
now sweating and swearing
'I've bloody well had enough!
What do you think I am, the door
mat of New York?
WELL, you're WRONG!'
she bellowed,
wiping out the Brooklyn Bridge in one go
(it was ugly, anyway.)
But then, the mayor of New York, who happened
    to be a famous superstar,
appeared and tried to reason with her.

'Look, Miss Lib, you're a tourist attraction and the
    symbol of America's liberty,
we can't afford to lose you!'
Her face went purple, and she screamed,
'DON'T give me that childish drivel about *liberty*,
you old-fashioned fool!
I quit! Find yourself a different dumb blonde to
    advertise your stupid country!'
And
on that note, the burly blonde flung round,
(accidentally catching her dress on an oil tanker
    which proceeded to sink)
and stomped off into the distance,
singing her own uncensored version of
the Star Spangled Banner.

Simon Wales (15)
Lichfield, Stockport,
Cheshire

The 1989 Cadbury's Poetry Competition

The Cadbury's Books of Children's Poetry contain about 200 selected entries from children of all ages and are illustrated with work from the National Exhibition of Children's Art.

If you would like to enter the 1989 competition whether in the Art, Craft or Poetry sections, you can write to this address for an entry form:

Cadbury's National Exhibition of Children's Art
Granby
Altrincham
Cheshire
WA14 5SZ

(Please enclose a stamped/addressed envelope)

Remember – you not only have a chance to feature in the *Cadbury's Seventh Book of Children's Poetry* but also to win a place on the Cadbury Italian Art Tour.

Index of titles

Index of authors